Praise

"*Out of the Cage* describes Shapiro's experiences with orangutans learning to live in the wild. The stories are captivating, and at the same time raise serious ethical questions about the way these highly intelligent beings are treated by us."

— Dr. Jane Goodall, DBE,
Founder of the Jane Goodall Institute &
UN Messenger of Peace

"To this day, I'm not sure anyone other than Dr. Shapiro has taught sign language to free-ranging juvenile and adult orangutans in their natural forest habitat. Remarkably, Gary carried on his work for years and tells the story in his compelling narrative."

— Gregory F. Tague,
An Ape Ethic and the Question of Personhood

"Gary's field notes and memories are transformed into a fantastic tale of adventure and discovery. .... If you ever doubted that any of the great apes (other than humans) are sentient beings, than [this is] a must read."

— Nancy Pearlman,
Global 500 Laureate,
United Nations Environment Programme

"With eloquence and heart, this book transports you deep into the lush forests of Borneo and the remarkable lives of orangutans. The author's pioneering research and steadfast advocacy have made an immeasurable impact. *Out of the Cage* is a stirring call to action that will leave you with a renewed appreciation for the critical work of conservation."

— Ed Begley Jr.,
actor and environmentalist

"If this wonderful, beautifully detailed book doesn't encourage you to work to stop rampant and global animal abuse, nothing will. Shapiro's compelling and deeply heartfelt personal stories, along with his detailed research on these sentient beings, clearly shows that the mistreatment of orangutans is a glaring scar on humanity's moral compass."

— Marc Bekoff, Ph.D.,
The Emotional Lives of Animals (2024)

"This is a book of sound science drawn from personal field experience, relayed endearingly to all[, as] Gary outgrows his cage...to become one of the foremost spokespersons for Orangutan protection, conservation and ethical treatment."

— Caroline Gabel,
Shared Earth Foundation

"Dr. Shapiro elegantly shares his experiences in the rainforest while including the personal struggles that he had to face. His fifty years of conservation knowledge makes it an important read, worth it for anyone...."

— Jack Dalton,
The Kid Conservationist

Out of the Cage

To Phyllis + Peter,
please think about
Marlene & her love of
orangutans when you
read my journey. I hope
you will understand her
commitment to these amazing
"persons of the forest" resonate
with a deeper love of nature
that is worth preserving

Gary E

Opening Note

What you are about to read is a deeply personal work and intact expression of its author's exploration of the truth. For this reason, we strongly encourage you to explore all of the details and implications of anything you discover or encounter as a result of this work.

In accordance with The Mad Duck Coalition's mission of encouraging and providing intellectual stimulation of all kinds, we cannot endorse any of the ideas presented by any individual member of our flock.

The only things we endorse are the authorial integrity of the works we publish and the quality of intellectual engagements that they produce and inspire.

Out of the Cage

My half century journey from curiosity to concern for the "person of the forest"

By Dr. Gary L. Shapiro

Ithaca, NY

2024 The Mad Duck Coalition ™ First Edition

THE MAD DUCK COALITION, its imprints, and colophones are trademarks of The Mad Duck Coalition, LLC.

For information about our special discounts for libraries, reviews, bookstores, and academic professionals, contact us through our form at thmaduco.org

Published in the United States under In The Weeds, an imprint of The Mad Duck Coalition, LLC, New York.

Paperback: 978-1-956389-13-5
Hardback: 978-1-956389-10-4
Epub: 978-1-956389-14-2

Library of Congress Control Number: 2024931705

www.themadduckcoalition.org

Dedication

I've put considerable thought into this acknowledgments section, reflecting on the individuals to include as my book took shape over the years. I initially considered putting everyone I could think of in microprint so they could see their name in black and white. After a discussion with my publisher about this idea, I've opted instead for brevity and hereby express my deep gratitude to all those who've supported me on my journey from initial curiosity to deep concern for the forest's red-haired inhabitants: to my cherished family, friends, colleagues, volunteers, Indonesian officials, talented photographers, skilled experts, and random people who I have bumped into along the way – you know who you are. I apologize that your name isn't mentioned individually. I hope you understand.

However, in the gestation of this project, I must extend my heartfelt thanks to Gregory Tague for his unwavering belief in my ability to write and publish this book, and to Jeffrey Krizman, the fearless editor and publisher of The Mad Duck Coalition, for daring to bring this book to life in print. Acknowledgments must also be given to Richard Haas, Paul Chaffee, Roger Fouts, Birute Galdikas and Rod Brindamour for opening the doors for me to enter the world of orangutans within and outside the cage. And of course, my sincere thanks to Inggriani Shapiro, my wife, for decades of unwavering support in my passion for orangutans.

Lastly, I wish to acknowledge my extended family of distant cousins, both living and deceased, dating back to our common ancestry 12 to 14 million years ago. You are an integral part of my "community of equals," and your enduring struggle to preserve your way of life in the forests, your ancestral home, is both inspiring and humbling. I hope that this book, in some way, contributes to supporting your ongoing fight for long-term survival.

Table of Contents

Murder You Say?

I was going to investigate a murder; I told the pilots. On my arduous, 20-plus-hour, multi-stop journey to Jakarta in Indonesia on June 17th from Los Angeles, I ended up telling the pilots all about how I ended up on this flight. After all, it wasn't uncommon for passengers back in those pre-9/11 days in 1978 to visit the cockpit to gaze at the instrument panel and to alleviate pilot boredom during the trans-Pacific crossing.

It all started back in Norman, Oklahoma about a year ago, I told them, where I was conducting research on the abilities of a juvenile chimpanzee named Ally to comprehend sequences of signs at the Institute for Primate Studies just outside of town. Jimmy Carter was recently inaugurated as President; the first episode of the "Star Wars" saga was a big hit in its first theatrical release; Elvis Presley, "The King of Rock and Roll", had died in mid-August, and my situation as a grad student at the University of Oklahoma barely kept me above the poverty line. As a result, I was very intrigued by a call from my major professor, Dr. Roger Fouts, about a special opportunity.

Fouts, well-known for his chimpanzee sign language program at the Institute, had just received a strange call from an even stranger woman whom he had first met at a conference in a secluded castle in Europe three years prior, Biruté Galdikas. She asked if Fouts thought orangutans could be taught sign language, like chimpanzees, and if he knew of anyone who could fly out to Borneo to do so. Given the previous research I had done teaching symbolic communication skills to Aazk, an orangutan at the Fresno Zoo, and now directly under Fouts with Ally, I was naturally the first person he thought to reach out to, or so he said.

It was when he surprised me at his university office that I heard the full details: Galdikas wanted to get one of her orangutans to confess to murder. She wanted an orangutan to confess to murder!

Fouts relayed what information he had: a lifeless body was found on the bank of the Sekonyer – a blackwater river in the middle of a primeval forest, in Galdikas's territory. One of her orangutan children, Doe, was dead: drowned. Cute little Doe. Newly arrived at Camp Leakey, Doe was one of the young orphans seeking a new life in that jungle outpost Galdikas ran with her husband, Rod Brindamour. How did she die? Accidental drowning? Murdered by the hands of another? Galdikas and her husband had suspicions, and a suspect, but the suspect, Sugito, wasn't talking. He was mute for all intents and purposes. That's why she had reached out to Fouts and why Fouts had reached out to me.

The money aside, which was barely enough to cover my expenses, I was excited by this opportunity, very excited! Borneo, murdering orangutans, sign language in the jungle? Although my major was Zoology, I was pursuing a Ph.D. on a topic that was more commonly associated with the field of comparative psychology. My cross-disciplinary interest in orangutans was there from the very beginning, having already long researched the symbolic communication abilities of an orangutan while taking graduate coursework for a master's degree in biology.

But, being blunt, let's be real: I was a twenty-five-year-old, recently divorced biologist with wanderlust and Borneo evoked the images of the naturalist Alfred Russell

Wallace, headhunters, and the "end of the earth" to me. Plus, no one had ever taught sign language to any ape in its natural world. And a murdering ape at that! Visions of Edgar Allan Poe's "The Murders in the Rue Morgue" often popped into my mind. So of course, I immediately accepted the offer to interview with Galdikas and her husband, which turned out to be a lot more involved than I thought: Galdikas was looking for a graduate student to go to Borneo and teach signs to Sugito as well as run her jungle outpost, the Orangutan Research and Conservation Project at Camp Leakey (named in honor of famous paleo anthropologist and archaeologist Louis Leakey) when she and her husband were away. For two whole years!

I immediately began sharing the news with my family, but they did not share my excitement at this opportunity, my grandmother especially. "Don't go! You will break your mother's heart," Bella Kaplan, my dear grandmother, implored after I explained what I was planning to do. This short stout woman and her husband, my grandfather David, two Eastern European immigrants from before World War II, were unable to appreciate the importance of what I was planning to accomplish: "It's just monkey business". That hurt. Over a cup of coffee and some Danish, I explained the monumental, pioneering research I would be conducting... to no avail. Nana, what my grandmother taught us to call her, immediately brought my mother into it, asking how she would feel, saying it would break her heart, but I had already spoken to my mother. She was an exceptionally strong woman who had a certain constitution when it came to challenges in her life, having divorced and protected my brother, sister and me from her husband/our abusive biological father, raising us single-handedly, and provided alimony to my disabled father. I had already got her support: she said, "I support whatever you really want to do in your life, even going to Borneo. Just be careful. And if you die out there, don't ask me to come to get you."

As interesting as family conflict was though, the pilots were more interested in the central question that started my journey: "Do you really think the orangutan would confess to killing another ape?" I wasn't sure, I replied, and that was true. I explained some of the background histories about great ape language studies, from the early days of the Kellogg's (1933) and the Hayes (1952) mostly failed efforts to teach vocal English to chimpanzees, to the breakthrough work of the Gardner's (1969) that opened up a channel of communication with a chimpanzee through the use of American Sign Language. Their student, Roger Fouts, eventually took Washoe, the first signing chimpanzee, to the University of Oklahoma and the Institute for Primate Studies, and hence, my academic connection, Fouts being my mentor, and big opportunity.

I told them about my idea of using signs to test if orangutans actually kept a "mental map" in their heads as to where ripening fruit was located within their home range. It was assumed that this was the case, as they sometimes make a beeline to preferred fruit trees, like durian, when the fruit on the tree is ripe enough to eat and getting to such valued resources before competitors would be a selective advantage.

My idea was to teach signs for valued foods and for colored containers which could be taken into different parts of the nearby forest. If I told the orangutan that the "sweet fruit" was "in the blue box" and the orangutan went straight to it without wandering randomly, it would add support to the theory of the "mental map." Orangutans have these large brains so it wouldn't be surprising if they would put it to such use.

I still have a tendency to stray from questions, but I explained that apes could learn to use signs to ask for foods, non-foods, and activities of interest. They could also learn to describe the properties of objects with signs. But what signs would need to be taught to minimally express the concept: "I killed Doe"? How would you teach the referents, items or actions that the sign represents? Moreover, I explained that, like humans, apes can and do lie and deceive, so even if I taught Sugito the concepts, why would he ever confess to it? To get a banana?? Would that even count as a confession? How would one ever prove such an admission even if the ape made signs suggesting it?

But, as I told the pilots, I was looking forward to answering those questions on the adventure of my life, one dominated by orangutans, not chimpanzees, and there were a lot of orangutans to study at Camp Leakey, which meant all the answers to all of my questions. I just didn't imagine that the adventure would become my life, a life filled with great joy and suffering, a life that, even as I write down my thoughts, makes my legs hop with excitement toward my next steps.

The plane arrived at Halim Airport in Jakarta and Nina Sulaiman, rector of the Universitas Nasional, greeted me warmly, directed airport porters to take my baggage to her car, and began orienting me as to what was in store for me during the next week or so. I was overwhelmed stepping into this sprawling southeast Asian city of over five million people. Nina, a tall Dutch woman who was married to a successful Javanese insurance salesman, was animated as she talked and weaved aggressively through the chaotic traffic. I had a hard time absorbing what she was saying as I clenched my seat with both hands and experienced the repeated fear and relief of near collisions while she navigated the busy streets. After the long trip, I was tired but excited while breathing in Jakarta's humid air and the sweet, pungent smell of clove-scented cigarette smoke in this very different cultural environment.

Nina and her family hosted Galdikas and Brindamour during their occasional trips to Jakarta, and as a result of their close relationship, Nina once again came to their aid, specifically my aid, along with her children who were directed to accompany me around the city, my personal interpreters. Besides her other administrative duties with the university, Nina also arranged for students from the department of biology to spend time in Camp Leakey and conduct research as part of their college education. It fit nicely with the government's mandate to have an Indonesian counterpart for each foreign scientist.

As Nina drove me to a Guest House where I would spend my nights during my first time in Jakarta, it didn't take long to form an impression of what Jakarta was like. A spread out, bustling megapolis with treelined boulevards, narrow streets lined with shops, and tall hotels with a mix of old Dutch homes and buildings. I also saw the abject poverty on display with makeshift shelters along rivers and canals, and dirty looking children and thin women in tattered batik sarongs begging on the street, tapping on our closed windows at traffic stops. Of course, it was much, much more, but I was tired. It was getting dark, and we eventually arrived at a Guest House Nina recommended in the center of the city, a low-cost hostel that provided temporary stays of missionaries, government workers, and academics. I met some of the people staying and learned their fascinating stories of their time in Indonesia, but after checking in, I crashed for the night.

Over the course of nine days, Nina and her family helped me get acclimated and provided many opportunities for me to interact with people and places in Jakarta. Despite my ambivalent feeling about Jakarta, I learned to appreciate some of its beauty and remarkable history that included a colonial Dutch presence for 350 years.

Most importantly, Nina and her family helped me visit the appropriate offices to get my permits and letters in order before heading to Kalimantan (Indonesian Borneo). There were a lot of offices that I had to visit: Home Affairs, Police, and the Indonesian Science Institute in Jakarta and the Forestry department, Science Institute and National Gardens in Bogor. In between office visits and in the evening, I was able to experience Jakarta's culture, cuisine, and points of interest with some of Nina's daughters. Her other relatives also seemed delighted to be showing me around this colorful capital city.

My visit coincided with the city's four hundred and fifty-first birthday celebration taking place between Hotel Indonesia and the lavish welcome monument and fountain in the center of town. Under former president Soekarno's rule, lavish monuments had been built all around the city. Rini, her sister Nani, and I stopped nearby to watch a marching band followed by observing a big parade from atop the now-closed President Hotel across the way. Later Rini and I jumped aboard a becak (pedicab) and walked the streets let to take in the smells and sounds of a place made famous a decade ago in "Year of Living Dangerously", a 1982 Mel Gibson drama-romance that takes place in Jakarta. It was exciting and breathtaking for a newcomer to Indonesia.

On another day, I was accompanied by Nina's niece, Hani, to the city of Bogor to visit the famous "Kebun Raya" botanical gardens, the National Biology Institute, and the Nature Protection office in the Forestry Department. I located one of Galdikas's former students, Sugardjito, in the Zoology building at the world-famous botanical gardens. Sugardjito, whose parents named him after boxer Sugar Ray Robinson, had just returned from Camp Leakey and was finishing up his degree. He warned me of the high likelihood of my contracting "falciparum" malaria if I stayed for a long time in the field, something that Galdikas never warned me of but which I probably fell victim to several months later. Jito, as he liked to be called, took me by motorcycle around town and to the National University campus in Jakarta days later.

The trip through Bogor was a combination of paying courtesy calls and doing the paperwork necessary to make my stay in Borneo both legal and official. Bogor was in the mountains south of Jakarta where the temperatures were several degrees cooler. Many of the ex-pat conservation and orangutan experts, like John MacKinnon and Herman Rijksen, made their homes in Bogor and commuted to the hotter metropolis of the capital. During lunch at Hani's parent's home, I learned a lesson of leaving valuables unattended even on the porch of a private home. My SLR camera "disappeared" causing me to increase my mindfulness when traveling around Indonesia, even before mindfulness became a popular concept.

During my time in Jakarta, I tried a lot of spicy food and tropical fruits, visited the Jakarta Zoo where I held an orangutan, spent the day at "Dream Island" an Indonesian theme park, and gave an impromptu lecture at the National University. These experiences helped shape my initial view about this exotic country where island names like Bali and Java could be more easily identified by most westerners than Indonesia itself.

One of the tropical fruits I was hoping to try was the famous stinky fruit, the durian – whose name means "spiny" in Malay and Indonesian, as it looks like a medieval mace. I had read about the amazing fruit in Alfred Russel Wallace's "Malaysian Archipelago" and was expecting something quite magical. But at the time I arrived in Jakarta, the fresh fruit was not in season, so the Sulaiman girls were able to get me a piece of dodol, the rendered down durian, mixed with rice flour and sugar. The candy reminded me of eating sticky asphalt with sugar, with a distinct sulfurous taste, not at all like what I would discover was fresh durian.

Still, I had the pleasure of experiencing Indonesian humor firsthand during a day trip to "Dream Island" with Nina's daughter, Nani and family friend, Yuni. They introduced me to the delicious taste of young coconut with its jelly-like meat inside the husk. As we sipped the refreshing coconut water through plastic straws, they playfully taught me some Indonesian words

They told me that the Indonesian word for coconut was "Kepala" and that the word for head was "Kelapa." I was grateful for the lesson, but boy was I in for a surprise! A few months later, I asked a Dayak vendor in Borneo for a coconut to enjoy, but the vendor looked confused. Frankly, he looked at me like I was crazy. It turned out that the correct word for coconut is, in fact, "Kelapa," and I had been walking around Indonesia the whole time asking for heads! Even worse, the Dayaks are the indigenous tribes of Borneo known for their fierceness and past headhunting tradition. A headhunting tradition! I was incredibly embarrassed when a Camp Leakey staff member told me I had been tricked.

In the end, despite the embarrassment, I couldn't help but laugh at myself and appreciate the playful nature of Nina's daughter and friend. They made my time in Jakarta enjoyable, but after weeks of processing papers, I was ready to head to Borneo for my next adventure.

Borneo Bound

On the morning of June 28, 1978, my heart was racing as I stood in line at the check-in counter, sweating profusely in the tropical heat. Despite my best efforts to negotiate a discount on my overweight baggage fees, I had to pay an exorbitant amount, but nothing could dampen my excitement for what lay ahead. As I flew across the Java Sea towards Borneo, the turbulence added an extra thrill to the journey, especially when I was jostled around in the cramped airplane restroom.

After landing near the bustling city of Banjarmasin, I couldn't believe my eyes as I saw hundreds of people outside the terminal. It was a surreal experience. I felt like an adventurer in a foreign land. From there, I took a taxi to the Rita Hotel, where I learned a painful lesson about the slippery porcelain tiles in the bathroom. But that was just a minor hiccup in an otherwise exciting journey.

At the hotel's coffee shop, I met Dean and Alexandra, two fascinating UNESCO workers who shared my passion for Indonesia. Over a sumptuous five-hour meal, we chatted about our respective work and interests, and I was thrilled to learn that they were heading to the same destination as me the next day. Meeting new people along the way was one of the most enjoyable parts of traveling in Indonesia, and I was always grateful for the chance encounters.

The next morning, we took a taxi together to the airport, but the vehicle got a flat tire on the way.

Thankfully, we managed to flag down another taxi and continued our journey. As I checked in for my flight to Palangka Raya, I couldn't help but feel a surge of adrenaline at the thought of flying on a twenty-seat de Havilland Twin-engine Otter. This plane was known for its ability to use shorter runways, making it perfect for the remote destinations I would be visiting.

The pilots flew the aircraft six thousand feet above the rainforest, low enough for me during the ascent and landing to get a breathtaking view of the individual forest canopies, occasional farmland, and winding river systems. I was transfixed, leaning against the small windows and taking it all in. As we started to descend, I squinted hoping to see an orangutan sitting in her day nest but the scene passed too quickly to make out anything like that. Soon we were in the provincial capital of Palangka Raya where foreign scientists had to get permission before heading to the field. Clutching a fistful of letters gathered in Jakarta, I had to visit the provincial government offices and register with the various agencies and get more letters to take to my last stop. I also was asked by Galdikas to meet Mr. G.T. Binti, an older gentleman of Dayak descent who was transitioning out of local government service. He had taken a liking to Galdikas and Brindamour years earlier treating them almost like his own children and helping them deal with sometimes difficult immigration and visa matters. Galdikas and Brindamour honored him by naming their first human child after Mr. Binti and insisted I pay him a courtesy call, a very important ritual in a country known for building and strengthening relationships through traditional personal meetings. For those of us conducting research and conservation activities within a protected area under the auspice of the government, meeting with officials like this gave them a chance to size up the foreigners and for us to determine who was excited, lukewarm, or antagonistic to our program. I was to learn it was important to make friends with people in government, even at the lowest levels, as they would inevitably rise in rank and become allies. For now, I was just getting started.

To meet Mr. Binti, I had to get to town. Luckily, I got a lift in a jeep from the Department of Education and Culture, generously arranged by Dean and Alexandra, that dropped me off at the Forestry Department building where I met two officials, introduced myself, and did the requisite chatting. One of the officials at the Forestry Department, a Mr. Koes, volunteered to become my driver and helped me to check-in at the Sakura Hotel in downtown Palangka Raya. After dropping off my luggage, we headed to the Immigration office looking for Mr. Binti. He wasn't there, so we drove to the provincial level office for Home Affairs, a security office like the FBI, where I submitted one of the numerous letters I obtained in Jakarta. Koes told me he would arrange for a meeting with Mr. Binti. With that, I thought everything was set and all my official paperwork was complete: so many letters dropped off at the Police, Home Affairs, Forestry, and Immigrations and I would be soon be off to Tanjung Puting. I was wrong.

Koes dropped me off at my hotel where I took a rest and got up for a snack. Then Alexandra and Dean showed up at about 2:30 pm to check-in. To reciprocate their kindness, Dean and I agreed to share my room, and I joined them for a lunch of sweet and sour chicken gizzards and vegetables on a bed of rice. It went down nicely with a glass of warm Bintang beer over ice. Later we walked all over town which attracted a large crowd of kids staring and tagging along with us, many wanting to practice their English. "Hello Mister," was commonly shouted out in my direction. I was thoroughly enjoying this attention of being novelty entertainment for the children. I learned that only about 50 westerners showed up each year in this provincial capital.

As we walked down the wide but dusty streets, we saw children playing in the streets, teenagers playing pool in the billiards hall, families bathing along the riverbank, and workers hauling various items to and from trucks and stores. In one of the small roadside stores, I bought 16-AA batteries for about $1.80 to make sure my Sony Walkman had enough power for several months. We returned back to the hotel at 5 pm where I waited an hour for my driver to pick me up to take me to Mr. Binti's home to do our customary courtesy call.

When we arrived at Mr. Binti's home, he greeted us and served sweet tea, and we sat and talked for about one hour. While being a very nice man, Mr. Binti didn't speak as much English as I presumed he did. Koes served as my translator and mentioned that another orangutan (about 1-year-old) was being sent back to Tanjung Puting Reserve today on the same flight we had arrived on. At some point, Mr. Binti called a local travel agent and it appeared there was no Saturday flight, but maybe a Sunday flight. On the way back to the hotel, we stopped at one of the airline offices and were assured if a plane was to leave before Monday, I would be called.

Back at the hotel, I met a friendly Indonesian English teacher who wanted to talk with Dean. We all sat together in the hotel lobby having some good conversation and snacks until going to the hotel dining room for a normal meal. There we were joined by an American student attending Stanford University. Hotels in Indonesia were and continue to be great places to meet interesting people. After returning to our room, I headed for the bathroom where I learned to use the squatting toilet for the first time, the kind I would use for almost the entire two years, particularly in the field.

I woke up the following day at 6:30 and had breakfast with my UNESCO friends. We all went our separate ways in the morning, I picked up my plane ticket, then reconvened to snack on deep-fried bananas in our hotel's lobby before walking to the Halmahera Hotel for dinner. There we feasted on crab and asparagus soup, steak and vegetables, and deep-fried crab. Excellent food for about $5.00 for each of us. At the restaurant, we met Jack, an Englishman working in Palangka Raya installing the city's telecom system. Jack told the unsettling story of his friend who was working on the project and died of a massive heart attack a few days earlier. The local officials claimed he had imbibed 100 bottles of beer which was surprising to Jack who claimed his friend wasn't even tipsy that night. I would later learn that such discrepancies like this were the stuff of Indonesia's opaque grapevine, particularly when it dealt with the government and politics.

The next day, I left for the airport barely an hour before the scheduled plane after a quick breakfast and saying a final goodbye to Alexandra and Dean. Those two fine folks wished me well as the hotel manager whisked me to the airport. During a frenetic moment at the airline check-in station, I wasn't sure I was going to make the flight, as they didn't seem to have my name on the list. Fortunately for me, Mr. Koes from Forestry met me at the airport and straightened things out. Thanks to his help, I departed on schedule. As it turned out, Mr. Koes Saparjadi, my occasional driver and translator, would decades later rise up in the ranks of government to become the Director General for Forest Protection and Nature Conservation for all of Indonesia, the top position overseeing activities related to biodiversity, forests, and conservation, just under the Minister of Forestry himself. Though our paths never directly crossed again, I often reminisce about the profound impact Mr. Koes had on my journey and his subsequent contribution to the preservation of Indonesia's natural treasures. It serves as a reminder of the remarkable journeys that life takes us on and the incredible transformations that can occur in the lives of those we me, et along the way.

In a little over an hour, we landed at Iskandar Airport just outside of Pangkalan Bun. I knew nothing about the history of the city or its layout when I arrived, but with the help of a friendly cigarette smoking young man, I took a public minibus with all my luggage to the Pangkalan Bun police station, located on the main road of Pangeran Diponegoro. Across the street was the St. Paul Catholic Church. The church was officiated by the Reverend Mohr who took frequent trips up the Arut River to convert the local animistic Dayak people to Catholicism, a holdover practice from when the Dutch colonized these outer islands.

I checked in with the police dropping off the suitcases of gear I brought with me. I met Mr. Nurhadi, the police chief, who had an infectious smile. He truly enjoyed meeting foreigners so he could practice his English and impress them with how he was taking good care of the local citizens. He was a civil servant assigned by the police in Jakarta to maintain the peace in Pangkalan Bun. While his staff was processing my paperwork, we spoke about my plans, his personal life (wife and kids) then whispered to me, "Do you want to see something interesting?" I said, "Sure", seeing this as a way to build a positive relationship with the top local police official. He then turned with his big smile and pointed to a black curtain in his office. He slowly opened the curtain revealing the dozens of passport-sized photographs of many of the Chinese Indonesian citizens he said he was monitoring. I couldn't help but wonder if this was a policy set up years before, following the ascent of Soeharto to monitor potential members of the Communist Party, but I didn't dare ask such questions, as talk of politics of this sort during the Soeharto era could be grounds for deportation.

After checking in with the police, I left my luggage with the guard, and Mr. Nurhadi took me to the office of the Forestry Department where I met Mr. Baharun, head of the local forestry. He spoke fairly good English, so I explained my reason for being in Indonesia and in Tanjung Puting in particular. He seemed very friendly and invited me to his home later in the evening, which I learned was where much forestry business was informally transacted in Pangkalan Bun. After excusing myself, I returned to the police office, picked up my luggage from the guard, and went across the street to the Catholic church where I met Sister Christensea, who was the biological sister of Pastor Mohr, the priest of this local church. Both he and his sister were from Germany and sympathetic to Galdikas's and Brindamour's mission in Tanjung Puting. They showed their Christian charity by allowing the Canadian researchers and their students to use their simple tool shed located behind the church as a place to bunk for the night. This act of kindness did help Galdikas and Brindamour save money on hotel accommodations when shopping or doing various activities in town. They called it Camp Pastor. It consisted of a couple of old mattresses, a hurricane lantern, and a single-burner kerosene stove with a tea kettle, all placed on the dirt floor of the shed. Camp Pastor was hot and stuffy, but it served its basic purpose.

A couple of Galdikas's Indonesian students, who also served as her counterparts (a condition of the research visa she was on), were on their way back to Jakarta. Djoharly and Boang had just completed a six-month stint at Camp Leakey; recruited with the help of Nina Sulaiman, they did their own study but also assisted Galdikas in spotting and tracking wild orangutans through the study area. Each had a wealth of experience from their stay in Tanjung Puting yet were looking forward to returning to their families on the island of Java and starting back to a student's life on the National University campus as well.

As I introduced myself to the students, we sat down and discussed our plans over a cup of sweet tea. To my surprise, the beverage had mosquito larvae swimming in it, but I didn't show any disgust. My own upbringing and appreciation of nature had taught me to adjust to imperfections. I informed them that I was taking over the responsibility of Camp Leakey until Brindamour returned in September, as Ibu Birute (Galdikas) was finishing up her degree in Los Angeles. In Bahasa Indonesia, "ibu" is the polite and respectful way to address a married woman with a child, and I even showed them the letter from the Brindamours to confirm it. After our conversation, I used the makeshift washroom/toilet to take a classic "mandi" bath, pouring water over my body with a large plastic ladle, the standard way of bathing at Camp Leakey when not in the river.

As I draped my newly washed self in a vibrant sarong, I longed for a brief but peaceful slumber on the musty and pungent mattress. With each creak and groan, I couldn't help but wonder about the many other students who had used this rustic shelter. And soon, I would be joining their ranks for a much longer stint as I set out into the depths of the forest, ready to embark on an adventure like no other! What secrets did the forest and the minds of orangutans hold? What dangers lurked in the shadows?

As the night settled in, I ventured out to the bustling night market with the two students, drawing quite a bit of attention from the locals, especially the curious children who had never seen a westerner besides Galdikas, Brindamour, the pastor, and his sister. The evening took a more serious turn when we headed to visit a forestry official for about an hour to see an orangutan caged up in his home. It was our responsibility to bring the animal to Camp Leakey the next day, and the anticipation was palpable.

From there, we went to Mr. Baharun's home where we were served sweet tea and discussed various matters, though admittedly, I was a bit bewildered by the language barrier. Despite the lingual gap, I kept my smile plastered on and nodded my head along as the students took the lead in conversation. It was then time for dinner, and the students led me to a Javanese restaurant where the food was absolutely scrumptious though even if the ice in my drink was a little questionable.

Having been away from Camp Pastor for five hours already, we then made our way to the home of another Forestry Department official, Mr. Beringin. This animated bureaucrat from Sumatra was intensely curious about my plans, eager to practice his English with me, and carried a strong sense of an Indonesian official's security. I sensed that he was sizing me up, but we soon found common ground over glasses of beer and tea while watching TV late into the night.

It was past midnight when we finally made our way back to Camp Pastor, and I felt a sense of relief knowing that I had passed some unspoken but polite interrogation.

Heading Upriver

We got up early the following morning, and I was picked up at Camp Pastor at 8:10 a.m. by Mr. Baharun, head of Forestry for this region of Borneo who had a caged orangutan in the back of his vehicle. We headed to the port town of Kumai some 15 km to the east over a mostly unpaved road. The orangutan and my suitcases and gear were dropped off at Mr. Yusran's home, which was across the street from the forestry office. Mr. Yusran worked directly under Mr. Baharun and was in charge of the local forestry office and activities in the nature reserve. Mr. Baharun then took two camp workers, Usman and Junai, and me back to Pangkalan Bun to do some shopping. We were dropped off at the main marketplace where we met with the students Djoharly and Boang as well as the old Chinese merchant, Apu. I gave Apu a letter from Brindamour, which he read not looking very pleased. Apu provided the Brindamours with a line of credit so they could shop for the various staples including drums of gasoline, 100 kg sacks of sugar and rice, and large bags of powdered milk for the orangutans at Camp Leakey. Apparently, Brindamour owed some money, and I did not have any on hand. It was an awkward encounter, the first of several I would have in the weeks ahead because of money problems waiting to be solved by Brindamour upon his return. Still, Apu let us get our items for Camp Leakey including rice, vegetables, batteries, flashlights, boots, and insect spray.

We then headed to the Dayak village of Pasir Panjang, where many of the Camp Leakey staff lived. Pasir Panjang means "Long Sands", and, indeed, the main road at the time was mainly a dry riverbed of white quartz sand. Pasir Panjang had been settled in Dutch colonial times, when the aboriginal Dayaks from the Ot Danum tribes were defeated by the Dutch and their Muslim-controlled sultans during an uprising and been taken to this area between Pangkalan Bun and Kumai, to be monitored as they assimilated into the new culture of the region. While some converted to Islam and Christianity, most of the descendants of the original Dayaks of Pasir Panjang continued to practice their animistic religion called Kaharingan (formally classified as Kaharingan Hindu by the Indonesian authorities) and many are employed at Camp Leakey to this day.

We picked up Gedol, a key camp staff member who was a skilled tree-climber and excellent orangutan tracker, and his wife Usip, who helped with cooking and cleaning at Camp Leakey. After fifty kilograms of bananas were loaded onboard for the ex-captive orangutans, we headed back to Kumai to purchase a 200-liter drum of gasoline. We loaded all of the supplies and gear into a longboat, a nearly 10-meter-long craft powered by a 40-hp Johnson outboard engine. The boat supposedly had a one-ton capacity, and we must have been close to that limit with the drum of fuel, sacks of supplies, luggage, and the five of us. It was decided that we would not bring the orangutan in a heavy cage back with us. We were already sinking mighty low in the water as it was.

After saying goodbye to Djoharly and Boang and making multiple pulls on the engine starter cable, the engine stopped its sputtering and we were off, but not for long. I started getting nervous as one of the crew, Junai, shifted his weight so much that the low-riding boat loaded with crew and supplies tipped too far causing it to take on water and the boat's opened tool chest to fall overboard. Pliers, screwdrivers, and wrenches disappeared into the shallow turbid water of Kumai Bay. Without these tools, we couldn't repair our unreliable engine during the 50-kilometer trip. Junai with a smirk on his face finally joined the local kids to go diving and eventually find all of the tools. While this was going on, Gedol and Usman kept trying to start the engine. Twenty minutes later, with the recovered tools and a running engine, we were underway, speeding across the now relatively calm and turbid waters of Kumai Bay towards the mouth of the Sekonyer River. I turned briefly to look back at this small town along the bay with Bugis schooners being built between jetties and the town mosque in the distance. With the wind in my face the 15-minute journey across the bay was exhilarating.

It was early afternoon as we entered the Sekonyer River, named after a pre-WWII sunken pirate ship that frequented these waters. My diary passage gives a taste of what that first trip upriver was like for me.

"Entering the river was easy (as I estimated it was about 40 meters wide) with submerged palms (Nipa spp.) on each side. Several times during the 2 ½ hour trip, the engine broke down but was finally repaired during the last 10 minutes of the trip where the river narrowed to 2 meters across. During the trip, I straddled the 200-liter gasoline drum like Slim Pickens in the film, "Dr. Strangelove". I kind of felt like him: not in knowing my eventual fate, but in enjoying the ride down. We passed countless 1, 2, and 3 room thatched structures along the river. Many people on the river make their living by fishing. Passed many beautiful Kingfishers - one was leading the way to Camp. The bird would dart in and out of the vegetation as we headed upstream. Saw many troops of golden brown and white proboscis monkeys feeding and carrying on in the trees along the riverbank. I believe I saw some langurs (*Presbytus spp.*) They were small-tailed monkey but they could have been immature proboscis monkeys. Proboscis monkeys are also called monyet blanda (Dutch monkeys) by the locals and Indonesians - perhaps a subtle way of immortalizing and commemorating the Dutch during the 350-year stay here."

The Sekonyer River is, as it was during my trip upstream, a blackwater river system, typical of many of the sinuous rivers in this low-lying region of Kalimantan as one heads inland. Such aquatic ecosystems are acidic in nature due to the breakdown of leaf litter in the rainforest watershed and the leaching out of organic acids which, like humic acid, provide a dark pigment that colors the actual water. A glass of the river water would appear almost like beer or urine in color, but through the water column appears like Coca-Cola. Surprisingly, the pigments in the water are dissolved (rather than suspended) so the water is transparent yet light is absorbed quickly within a few meters' depth.

The lush and vibrantly green Nipa palms line the mouth of the river and form the dominant vegetation for many kilometers upriver providing a resource for humans and wildlife alike. The thick feather-like leaves of the palm provide thatch for the roofs of the huts and simple buildings along the river, while birds and monkeys forage on the small fruit bunches of the palm. The water in this portion of the river is brackish with the seawater mixing with the acidic freshwater entering the bay during the tidal shifts. The water in the main branch of the Sekonyer River has also grown cloudier over the years due to suspended sediments originating from the disturbed watershed upriver; mainly from agriculture and mining activities outside and occasionally within the protected area.

About 10 kilometers upriver, the vegetation starts to change with lush aquatic riparian plants "rasau" and "bakong" from the *Pandanus* and *Hanguana* genera beginning to appear among the Nipa palm. Further upstream, these riverine plants become more dominant while the Nipa no longer tolerate the more acidic waters and disappear. Other trees species become present along the river providing both feeding and sleeping sites for long-tailed macaques and proboscis monkeys that normally congregate along the river before nightfall.

Zipping upriver mid-day in the longboat felt magical as each turn along the sinuous river revealed a new viewscape of trees and lush vegetation while the generated wind and bright sunlight forced me to squint. We quickly passed by the Sekonyer Village, an enclave relocated from within the reserve to the other side of the river. I had so many questions about the riverside settlements we passed along the way but those questions had to wait. After traveling about 40 kilometers upstream from the mouth of the river, we slowed down and headed up the right branch of the river that would lead into Tanjung Puting Reserve along peat swamp forests, and past submerged meadows and stands of tall trees for the last 8 kilometers of the journey. The clear blackwater from the right branch looked distinctly different from the more chocolate-colored water of the main branch and the zone of mixing was impressive.

The riverine trees created a canopy that cast an imposing shadow in the channel of this narrower portion of the tributary. The echo of the engine from the sounds of the pistons popping was also loud and deafening. Winding along the deeper part of the channel, the blackwater was more mirror-like and the river was only a couple of meters wide.

The last couple of kilometers before Camp Leakey, I passed the "lakes" area which were essentially depression lakes that form during the rainy season. The lakes at that time were expansive grassland areas with scattered stands of rasau and mats of bakong along the side of the river. Occasionally we passed flattened mats that were used by the crocodiles to sun on, according to the Camp Leakey staff.

During the last part of the trip to Camp Leakey, the river widened significantly to about 15 meters from shoreline to shoreline near the camp's landing, then the longboat pulled in next to the floating platform at the end of the long ironwood boardwalk leading to the buildings at Camp Leakey. The sturdy but narrow walkway, raised above the seasonally swampy shoreline, made accessing the camp relatively safe and easy. In the days before the walkway, Brindamour and Galdikas had to walk through the peat and swamp to get to high ground.

As we tied the boat off, I noticed four free-ranging orangutans across the river. They appeared as interested in us as I was with them. One of the orangutans was the infamous Gundul, the orangutan who Galdikas witnessed "raping" a former cook who worked at Camp Leakey. From his size, he didn't appear to be the terror I thought he would be. Another orangutan was an adult female named Rinnie, who had arrived from Jakarta and been at Camp Leakey for several years. I would come to know Rinnie very well in the months ahead.

Gedol, the most experienced Dayak assistant, gave out a loud cry, "Key yoh!" to announce to the staff at Camp we had arrived. Soon two camp workmen, Polis and Dolah, came to the landing along with a Celebes macaque, plus a baby Malaysian sun bear following from behind. Both animals watched as we hauled the supplies off of the boat and carried them the 200 meters from the river to the dining hall and storage area in Camp. It was hard work, as the sacks of rice and sugar weighed over one hundred pounds each. Once we unloaded the supplies, I was given the key and taken to the government-built guest house, a wooden structure with three bedrooms and two common rooms, to unload and unpack my suitcases. Knowing I was there for the next two years, I decided to take the largest room, something Galdikas didn't want me to do, but I was the only person staying in the structure and I really needed the space.

As I unpacked, King Kong, the name given to a needy sun bear, tried chewing my suitcases. I distracted him by grabbing his stretchable skin and fur. He immediately tried mouthing my index finger. After letting him suck my finger, something he would have been doing with his natural mother, I finally chased him out before returning to the river for a quick swim. It was already getting dark.

Soon enough, I returned back to my room, changed into my gray-blue jumpsuit, and with flashlight in hand wandered the trail back to the dining hall to have dinner with the crew, a meal that would become very common: rice, vegetables, some fish, and noodles. Only the hot sauce (sambal), vinegar, and soy sauce added different flavors. After dinner, I worked on my language skills with the crew and gave them a letter from Rod Brindamour which introduced me as the vice director of the Orangutan Research and Conservation Project until he returned. The crew read the letter and a few gave me big smiles. I understood I was new and untested, but I could sense they wanted to show me respect for the position I was given by Brindamour, a man they deeply admired. As I wandered back to my room in the dark, I felt elated. This first day was amazing for a 26-year-old kid from California in the middle of the jungle, and there was oh so much more in store for me.

Camp Leakey was home for me during my initial two years in Indonesia. You can actually see it on Google Earth today, though, during the late 1970s, it looked quite different with buildings and structures not then present.

Camp Leakey was named in honor of Louis Leakey, famed paleoanthropologist and archaeologist whose discoveries of early hominids in Olduvai Gorge established Africa as the cradle of humanity. It was Louis Leakey who set Jane Goodall, Dian Fossey, and Biruté Galdikas, the so-called Trimates, on their respective journeys to study chimpanzees, gorillas, and orangutans. Leakey felt confident that women primatologists would be less threatening to the animals than men, and that they would be more likely to gain the animals' trust while developing an understanding of the behavioral and ecological relationships between great apes and early hominids. Camp Leakey was Galdikas's homage to the man who helped get her started in Indonesia.

Camp Leakey might as well have been an island, as it is situated in a peat swamp forest where boats are the only way for the common person to access the outpost, located fifty kilometers from the town of Kumai.

There are two docks and walkways now at Camp Leakey which are both constructed with endangered and valuable ironwood: the original government-built dock and boardwalk constructed in the mid-1970s and the new dock, built in the 1990s by foreign volunteers helping with construction projects at Camp Leakey. The wood is extremely resistant to degradation but difficult to work with. The docks and walkways are perhaps the most valuable structures in all of Camp Leakey. Without them, staff would need to walk through the swamp emanating from the main channel of the Sekonyer tributary at least one hundred meters until they found higher ground. Carrying sacks of rice and sugar from the river to Camp was no longer an issue after their construction.

The boardwalk proved to be a technological benefit to improving the ease of travel to and from the river as well as a point of concern when orangutans, especially adult orangutans, would appear from underneath at a moment's notice. Large males could easily block one's travel to Camp from the dock, especially Kusasi or some of the other dominant cheek padders who claimed Camp Leakey as their territory. Adult females could also easily ambush staff and visitors alike, so seeing a large hairy hand appear and quickly grab an ankle was not a rare event.

The first building at the end of the boardwalk and after the small rise was the wooden director's quarters normally occupied by Brindamour and Galdikas. They had moved from a hut during the early days to this building made of four outer walls and a roof with inner walls separating the living room, the bedroom, the main office, and storage areas. This is where we would meet for evening drinks (non-alcoholic generally) and conversation. The building included a small library, a medicine and storage area for lab and photographic equipment. Continuing north along the small path through a portion of an abandoned rice field were the PPA quarters and the holding cages for the youngsters. PPA was the name of the branch of Forestry at the time responsible for maintaining Tanjung Puting, then a nature reserve.

Also, near the end of the boardwalk and headed east past the director's quarters was the well-known dining room, complete with a wash area, kitchen, storage room, and a large dining area, all proper. This was where we would go for meals, presentations, and work during the day on occasion. The large picnic tables and benches made it possible for several dozen people to dine together; indeed, our entire staff would generally dine together at breakfast and dinner. Lunch in the dining hall was informal as staff would generally be in the field at midday with their box lunch.

Just to the south of the dining hall were the staff quarters, sometimes called the longhouse, a series of simple, elevated rooms arranged linearly with a deck and small guard rail fence in front of each room. Used mostly for sleeping, the rooms served as many of the staff's private quarters. Free-ranging, ex-captive orangutans would make use of the space under the various buildings, like the dining hall, the long-house, the director's quarter, etc.

Toward the forest from the long house, there was a trail that meandered southeast through a small forest patch and then into an opening where the guest house was built. This was constructed by the Indonesian government for visitors to Camp Leakey, but it became my abode for the next two years and when I returned to stay in Camp six years later until Galdikas claimed it as her own residence. As mentioned, the guest house had a living room, three bedrooms, two storage rooms, and a bathroom with a squat toilet. There was even a working water pump in front of the bathroom to provide water for washing and bathing. The pump became a point of interest for the resident orangutan population who liked to take drinks from it, their own little water cooler.

Across the forest to the north of the guest house was the student housing. Like the guest house, the Student House was a multi-room building for multiple guests. Unlike the guest house, the Student House was very rough in its finish, something perhaps suited to students but not guests from Bogor or Jakarta.

Going north from the director's house, as mentioned, was a trail that went through a former rice field past a very short, forested area and opened up to a clearing; here the PPA house and the holding enclosure area was located. Just beyond that was a raised trail called Jalan 19 that led toward a feeding station nearly one hundred fifty meters to the north. The trail to the feeding station was made of wooden planks, as the entire stretch was a peat swamp forest.

The buildings were all connected by a series of trails that were used by humans and non-humans alike. The most widely used trail going into the forested study area was Jalan Toges, a wide, flat trail that led through the former "ladang" or dry rice field that was used by squatters before Galdikas and Brindamour arrived. Then the trail passed through a relict forest area and eventually to a network of hundreds of kilometers of cut trails Brindamour and staff created over the first four years of Galdikas's orangutan study.

First Contact: Meeting Rinnie

My first full day at Camp Leakey started after a difficult first night sleep in the humid forest with no fan or AC, but I got used to waking up with a coating of sweat. I went to the detached bathroom at the end of the guest house to wash up, then stepped off the porch, looked up at the popcorn clouds in an otherwise blue sky drifting eastward, and headed down the sand and dirt path towards the dining hall some fifty meters away through a small patch of forest. Camp staff were already eating the leftovers of the savory vegetables, fish, and rice served the night before. I joined them at the communal dining table and bench with a plate of food and did my best to make small talk. Some of the staff, mainly Dayak trackers, were already being given assignments by Gedol to search for orangutans in the study area as part of Galdikas's long-term orangutan research program to unravel the ecological and behavioral mysteries of the great ape residents in this part of Borneo.

After breakfast, Gedol, himself a skilled Dayak tracker and tree-climber, accompanied me to conduct an inventory of everything in Galdikas's and Brindamour's wooden house. I took notice of the medicine cabinet and a dart gun used to anesthetize orangutans. I avoided entering their bedroom.

I then wandered down the boardwalk searching for Sugito, the adolescent male orangutan whom I was originally asked to teach signs in order to extract a murder confession. After reaching the end, I climbed the partially covered ironwood tower that stood nearly 80-feet tall to get an overview of the area beyond the river. Some of the ironwood planks were missing and I found myself stepping carefully over orangutan dried feces and old banana peels left behind. Like the boardwalk, the tower was a government make-work project as some forestry official years earlier was impressed by fire watch towers in the Pacific Northwest and thought it would be a great idea to have a watch tower in this remote part of the Tanjung Puting forest. Such towers are usually built on hillsides overlooking distant ridges. Unfortunately, none existed at Camp Leakey so the view was limited. Consequently, unlike the invaluable boardwalk, the tower was used almost exclusively by ex-captive orangutans to escape from others or just relax on as they might in one of the trees below. But following my climb, I was exhilarated by the landscape below and the verdant rainforest canopy before my eyes. Mist was clearing downstream and an occasional kingfisher would fly effortlessly down the river corridor. Below me off the rickety floating dock were Camp Leakey staff bathing and washing their clothes. Laughter and mostly unintelligible chatter punctuated the cool morning air along with the occasional sounds of insects and birds. As I slipped climbing a step, someone below yelled, "Hati hati, Mr. Gary" which meant be careful. I yelled back, "Terima kasih", thank you, to them.

There was no sign of Sugito. I did however see the infamous Gundul across the blackwater river along the shoreline of the large expanse of peat swamp forest that was used to isolate some of the older and troublemaking ex-captive orangutans from the Camp Leakey side. I also saw Rinnie, an adult, female orangutan wandering along the river shoreline.

I returned to my room at the guest house and changed into my swimming attire, then I headed back to the river for a quick swim. I was curious about what lurked within the blackwater river and beneath the floating docks. As a SCUBA diver and former marine biology major, I enjoyed the thrill of encountering sea creatures, vertebrates and invertebrates, but what would I find in the remote river? Most local people feared crocodiles, especially the saltwater variety, and the smaller false gharials. The thought of encountering one of these large reptiles both excited and frightened me. I brought Brindamour's snorkeling mask and fins with me. After slipping gently into the cool, dark water, I held my breath and swam to the bottom which was only about 8 feet deep. Once my eyes adjusted to the twilight-like darkness, I scanned the bottom of the river holding onto a sunken log and soon encountered two sizeable creatures, a 3-foot dragonfish (*Scleropages formosus*) and a 4-foot freshwater Bornean turtle (*Orlitia borneensis*). When they spotted me just inches away, both quickly swam into the darkness. I felt ecstatic as my heart raced.

I pulled myself out of the water and sat on the edge of the 3-meter floating dock while some of the staff were still bathing nearby, then I turned my attention across the river to Rinnie and wondered if she might be my first student, assuming I couldn't find Sugito.

Rinnie was completely healthy with a thick coat of rusty-colored hair and a confident, wide gait as she wandered quadrupedally along the shoreline and in the shallows in search of cassava roots that were thrown to the ex-captive orangutans the previous evening. Cassava is a staple tuber crop in Indonesia and is easily grown on the infertile soils of the island of Borneo. Other smaller orangutans gave her wide berth, obviously deferring to her dominance among the group of ex-captives across the river from Camp. Rinnie picked up a cassava root with her free hand and used her broad incisors to rasp off the brown covering before biting deeply into the crunchy, white pith. I wondered what the raw tuber tasted like. I decided that I would sample some to find out. Unlike neophobic orangutans, I was never one to avoid new things.

I stood on the floating dock, watching and imagining the excitement of meeting this adult orangutan on her own terms and not in a cage. When could I actually interact with Rinnie, possibly begin teaching her signs? At that time, nobody had even started teaching an adult ape sign language, l, et alone an adult orangutan. Moreover, I didn't know if Rinnie would consider me a threat if I approached her. I had just gotten to Camp after all and most studies used young apes, infants or juveniles. The reason this was such a concern is because orangutans are extremely strong, five to eight times pound per pound compared to humans. Even a large adolescent can easily maim an adult human if they feel threatened.

Still, the opportunity whipped around my thoughts before I dove back into the cool, clear, tea-colored water that flowed past camp. When I came up, I happened to see Rinnie sitting placidly with a cassava root in hand and mouth. There was something about that, I just had to know. I couldn't wait any longer. I decided to enter this orangutan's personal space. My heart started to race with excitement as I moved slowly to the opposite side of the river. I was here to interact with the ex-captives and this was as good a time as any.

As I neared the shore, I found myself unable to quickly stand upright on the riverbank because of the fallen branches and decomposed woody debris that made up the bottom. In fact, the mucky part of the riverbank was such that I sank to my knee or thigh as I tried standing up on the boggy material. I felt totally helpless as I extracted myself from the muck and I climbed up to drier ground on all fours, not unlike the clambering movements of an orangutan, though the forest along the shore was covered with branches and logs that made travel a bit easier than on the mostly mushy peat.

I picked up a piece of cassava I found in the shallows and approached Rinnie. I figured I would come bearing gifts. It typically worked with people and dogs. I held it out towards her only a couple of meters away from me, and she immediately began ambling in my direction on all fours without hesitation. Once she got close to me, she stopped, stood up on two legs, gazed into my face, and reached out with her right hand. I couldn't believe it! Her brown eyes were fixed on me. I could hear her breathing and smell her earthy odor. I gave her the root and she began eating my first offering of food without hesitation. In the months to come, I would bring more tasty morsels, including pineapples, milk, rambutan, and bananas, to her as part of my research to serve as referents and rewards when teaching signs. That was a special first day–Rinnie had made contact with me, and more importantly, I had made contact with her.

I found out later that Rinnie's journey to Camp Leakey was typical of most ex-captives: poachers most likely killed her wild mother and smuggled her to Java where she was sold or given to a high official, some retired general in Jakarta, and had come into the care of Rod and Biruté in 1975. Life in the forest was challenging for Rinnie, as she had experienced the trauma of falling out of a tree resulting in a broken arm. It may have explained one of the reasons she preferred to spend much of her time on the ground.

As she sat and ate the cassava, I touched the coarse hair on her shoulder and arm. She didn't recoil or move away. She just sat there looking at me intently, perhaps wondering what I was going to do. I slowly reached for her right hand that was freely moving. She moved it out of the way but I persisted and gently corralled it with both of my hands. She complied as I took her free hand and began molding it into the sign for "come-give." Molding refers to the shaping and moving of the student's hand or hands by the teacher. She seemed attentive and did not act aggressively towards me as I moved the fingers of her hand making a beckoning gesture. After I molded her hand, I moved slightly toward her so she would associate the gesture with my response. While still holding her hand, I stepped back a foot or so, repeated molding her hand, and then moved toward her again. This cycle of molding and moving was to teach her that the sign meant for me to come to her. The molding of the hands followed immediately by the demonstration of a specific referent was the essence of the sign learning process. She looked at me briefly then turned her head away toward an approaching juvenile orangutan. Despite her distraction, she didn't leave. Here I was on my first full day at Camp Leakey teaching the action sign, "come-give" to an adult, free-ranging orangutan in the forests of Borneo, something no one had ever done before. Although I was elated by this progress, I couldn't share my excitement or at least explain why it was so amazing to any of the local staff in Camp as my command of Indonesian was still rudimentary. Unfortunately, I would have to wait for over two months to do so.

The rest of my first full day at Camp Leakey was indicative of what was to come: an always surprising set of unplanned encounters and issues between orangutans and humans, sometimes showing up without any notice.

Indeed, after I swam back to the dock after working with Rinnie, a canoe with four locals paddled upriver to our dock with bags of cassava. They were simple Melayu farmers who lived in the fields just outside the Tanjung Puting reserve. Two smiling women covered in simple batik scarves to protect them from the sun and their husbands who paddled the canoe transferred the heavy bags of cassava to the boardwalk later to be weighed. I noticed the women's teeth were red from the common practice of chewing betel nut quid. While most men smoked cigarettes, women chewed betel. They would make a small package or quid of areca (betel) nut and slaked lime wrapped in a betel leaf, place it in their mouth, chew it slowly and enjoy the slightly stimulating and narcotic effect. Copious amounts of red saliva from the lime/nut combination and reddened teeth resulted from this locally accepted practice. I came to find the blood-red splattering of their saliva along dirt walkways a disgusting reminder of this traditional practice.

Regardless, they also brought pineapples, sugar cane, and other crops that were easily grown in the relatively infertile soils by farmers and brought to Camp Leakey to be traded for rice, processed sugar, and kerosene, based on an agreed-upon exchange rate. When Camp Leakey staff went shopping in town, hundreds of pounds of these essential supplies were purchased so selling small amounts to nearby farmers and fishermen made it easier for them and built good relations among the locals. This mutualistic arrangement also provided us with fresh vegetables and fish for camp staff and a supply of basic foods for the ex-captive orangutans.

As I walked back to Camp along the lengthy boardwalk, I finally caught a glimpse of Sugito, suspended by one arm from a nearby tree. He kept his distance, but as the new white male human at Camp Leakey, I couldn't shake off the feeling that he seemed wary of me. The reason for my being there – to teach and interrogate this adolescent male great ape, who had been accused of murder – weighed heavily on my mind. The dark thought lingered as I wondered, did he really kill little Doe?

Despite the weight of this thought, my mind drifted to the other orangutans at the rehabilitation center who were learning survival skills on their own. Perhaps, some of them, like Rinnie, could become willing students if Sugito was, indeed, unworkably hostile. My first full day at Camp Leakey continued with me watching staff give milk to the eight or nine young orangutans in the elevated, outdoor safety enclosures near the forestry house. This is where they stayed protected from the wild pigs and pythons when not taken out and monitored by Camp staff. One infant named Toro was coughing and sneezing. After I noticed the others eating his discharged mucus, I had Toro isolated into a separate enclosure and prepared a concoction of tetracycline dissolved in milk. I was briefed about respiratory infections before arriving at this jungle outpost and realized that dispensing antibiotics and other medications would be part of my duties. I was assisted by one of the staff who helped me hold Toro. We had to be patient and coax him to drink as much of the medicated milk as possible. The rest was refrigerated until later. These were the conditions at a time before clinics and PPE. Afterwards, I headed to the dining hall to join the staff for lunch. The cuisine looked to be more of the same as breakfast. There would be no fine dining at this jungle outpost.

I returned to my room at the guest house to put up some posters and unpack more items. Gedol walked into my room unannounced and watched me silently. It was a bit creepy. I sensed he was sizing me up in his own way. Galdikas and Brindamour put me in charge of Camp in their absence, and he had read Rod's letter I presented the night before that put my assignment in writing. He excused himself and left leaving me to wonder. But my uncomfortable feeling soon gave way to appreciation. I clearly needed some shelving in my room, and Gedol must have saw that and acted. He returned along with

Dolah, a Melayu worker from a downstream village, and Usman, a Javanese assigned to Camp by the Forestry Department. They brought some prefabricated wooden shelves and installed them on the far wall. We spoke in broken English, as my fluency in Bahasa Indonesia was still limited, but I knew enough to say "terima kasih", thank you, to them for their kind deed, then presented them with a dart board I brought from the States, suggesting they install it in the dining hall.

It was getting later in the afternoon when Gedol and I headed to the river for a bath but found ourselves swimming downstream to look for a prau, a canoe-like boat, and one of our two longboats that Gundul, the notorious adolescent orangutan, apparently stole. Boat theft by orangutans was a common problem as the observant great apes quickly learned how to make use of this technology to ferry themselves by "hand paddle" across the river. Wading across this deep river to socialize with other orangutans was dangerous for a species too dense to swim or float across. Snatching boats was safer but required them to use their intellect to make use of the boats. We soon found the longboat Gundul "borrowed" about 100 meters downstream in the weeds and called for help. A few minutes later, Polis, who came into view with the other longboat still carrying the drum of gasoline we had brought to Camp the day before. As he approached us, Polis nearly capsized the boat as the drum rolled and shifted its weight. We paddled all three craft back to the center of the river across from the dock, tied them up to a long stout stick serving as anchor, and swam back to Camp side. With these important conveyances retrieved, I felt a sense of accomplishment and while somewhat fatigued, realized I could work side-by-side with the camp staff to solve problems. Keeping clever orangutans away from our valuables was to become part of my life for two years.

We walked down the boardwalk in the rain to the dining hall for a snack of deep-fried cassava chips. They tasted like hearty potatoes and were absolutely delicious. I still hadn't tried raw cassava yet, but that could wait. It was nearing 5 pm so I took the rest of the medicated milk from the refrigerator and warmed it up before bringing it to Toro, the sick orangutan. When we arrived at the enclosure area, we discovered all orangutans had escaped. Gedol and I searched and found the sick youngster in a nearby stand of trees with the other rehabilitants. I was later to learn that one of the adult orangutans, Siswoyo, probably unlocked the enclosures to help free them. Toro wouldn't come down by our calling to him, so we left him in the trees with the others to spend the night.

On my way back to my room at the guest house, I stopped by the staff quarters and tried speaking to some of the staff who returned from the forest. They were taking off their wet clothing and smoking clove-scented cigarettes. Apparently, they were following a wild orangutan. I was interested to know more about what they saw but was having a problem communicating with them. I decided I would bring my "kamus", my dictionary, to dinner.

Back at the guest house, I saw the notorious Sugito on the roof ripping off shingles. I yelled at him, scaring him off the roof and into the forest behind the building. It was time for him to make his night nest anyway. I changed my wet clothes and returned to the dining hall once the dinner bell rang. After a dinner of fried fish, vegetables, noodles and hot tea, I pulled out my "kamus" and the young men, Gedol, Usman, and Junei, were helping me learn Indonesian and I their English. At some point during our group conversation, I came up with a surprising proposal, even to myself. I demonstrated to them the method for teaching sign language to orangutans and announced that they were going to help me instruct the orangutans in this form of communication. For over two hours they sat transfixed as I gesticulated and looked up words in the kamus trying my best to explain what I was there to do for two years. They actually seemed enthusiastic, and I found myself learning Indonesian very rapidly that night.

Later that evening I returned to the guest house feeling ecstatic about this first full day in Tanjung Puting Reserve. I felt accepted by the staff as the assistant director of Galdikas's Orangutan Research and Conservation Project at Camp Leakey. I saw so much, interacted with orangutans, dove in the river, encountered local people, felt the generosity of the camp staff, and even got stung by one of the aggressive fire ants. But important to my being there, I met and tried teaching signs to an adult orangutan. Before going to sleep, I sat by lamplight at the large table in the living room of the guest house and spread out several small leaves I had brought back to the room earlier in the evening. I examined each one and counted the number of indentations I had marked with my fingernail on the leaf surface each time I molded Rinnie's hands to the sign, "come-give." It was my makeshift effort to keep track of the number of times she received training on a particular sign. I transcribed those data onto paper and decided that I would visit her again to see if I could continue to teach her signs. But tomorrow was already planned: I would go into the forest study area with Gedol, explore the cut trails, and follow a wild orangutan.

In the days and weeks that followed this initial encounter, I found myself swimming across the river several days a week to meet with Rinnie for signing lessons. I wanted Rinnie to be available and engaged at these lessons, so before heading to the river, I stopped at the dining hall and prepared some food and drink, usually rice, pineapple, and milk. My previous experience with orangutans suggested they were highly motivated by food. These edibles were placed into repurposed, plastic hot sauce bottles that were in turn crammed into used, cut-off pantyhose that my Aunt Ethel gave to me for my trip to Borneo. I also brought items that would serve as referents to the signs I was to teach her. I tied the nylon bag around my waist, headed down the boardwalk to the landing, and jumped into the cool blackwater river. Treading water, I slowly made my way over to the other side and crawled onto a dry log.

"Rinnie!" I would call at the top of my lungs. "Rinnie!" again I would call and wait to listen for the rustling of leaves and branches in the distance. Unless she was deep in the forest, Rinnie would eventually make her way through the canopy highway and down to the dry log or ground I chose as the day's classroom. Orangutans do learn their names and, indeed, understand a great deal of spoken language even though they are unable to articulate our words.

For up to an hour, Rinnie would sit and allow me to manipulate her hands into various configurations while showing her an item or demonstrating an action. I would ask her in vocal Indonesian, "Apa ini?" or "What's this?" before molding her hands. I repeated these actions almost every day making sure to groom her or scratch her between any given set of trials.

After the first week of training, I was instructing Rinnie on various signs, and within the first month, Rinnie was learning not only to make signs, but she also began to make basic sign combinations. I didn't share my data books with anyone at Camp so her progress wasn't understood or appreciated by some of our staff who occasionally watched my interactions with Rinnie from across the river.

My repetitious use of the phrase "Apa ini" to prompt Rinnie to name a referent proved to be comical with one of the Dayak cooks who was bathing topless on the floating dock across the river. "Mr. Gary, apa ini?" the cook cried out. I turned to see her clutching one of her large breasts while making the sign for "what's this" after which she gave out a hearty laugh. This, obviously, was not the behavior of a refined Indonesian woman; however, it showed that some of our staff felt comfortable enough, even this married women, to joke around with me as if I were part of her native village.

What was also fascinating was that Rinnie had come to understand that a sign, especially an iconic sign, could be created by taking the action referent and abbreviating it with a few movements. So repeated scratching (an action referent) could be abbreviated to scratch a part of the body one time (the sign for scratch). This happened for the sign "scratch" and "groom" as well. Rinnie created those signs; they were not trained to her with repeated teaching steps. She came up with them on her own.

In time, Rinnie even created her own sentences. For example, she made a sequence of movements, first reaching towards me with her right hand sometimes touching my arm, then touching an area of her body, and making a couple of scratching movements, the equivalent of "You scratch there." It was clear that not only could she learn how to name items of interest to me (such as when I was teaching her sign vocabulary), but she could create signs to ask for activities of interest to her. I spent many hours with Rinnie, introducing her with new referents and signs and trying to get the signs to be elicited in good form, as when I asked her, "What is this?" She would tolerate this type of training, sometimes only for the food and drink that was provided. But her interest frequently was not there, and the data on eye contact showed that Rinnie avoided eye contact during the crucial moment of molding the sign in front of the referent (Shapiro & Galdikas, 1995). How, then, could I teach her signs that did not rely on food or drink as the referent? It proved difficult.

I also asked Rinnie, and the other orangutans, "Apa mau?" or "what (do you) want?" This question did not require a specific response, as with asking to identify a referent (e.g., "apa ini"). They would usually sign, "that food" or "that drink" but once the food and drink were exhausted, the signing would be "you scratch" or "you groom."

Rinnie would sometimes stay at the makeshift classroom after the food was exhausted. She would then sign for me to scratch, groom, or brush her hair. She might do this for several minutes to a quarter-hour, depending on her mood, the weather, and if other orangutans were in the area.

Gallery One

1. Juvenile Sugito, the orangutan suspected of murdering Doe.

2. Washoe the 1st signing great ape at the Institute for Primate Studies in the 1970s.

3. Ally, my juvenile chimpanzee student, signs "leash" during a signing lesson.

4. Me holding Aazk at the Fresno City Zoo in the early 1970s.

5. Patiently waiting for Aazk to finish her play on the swing to return to her lesson.

6. Aazk makes a selection of symbols and hands them to me. Later she would put them on the board.

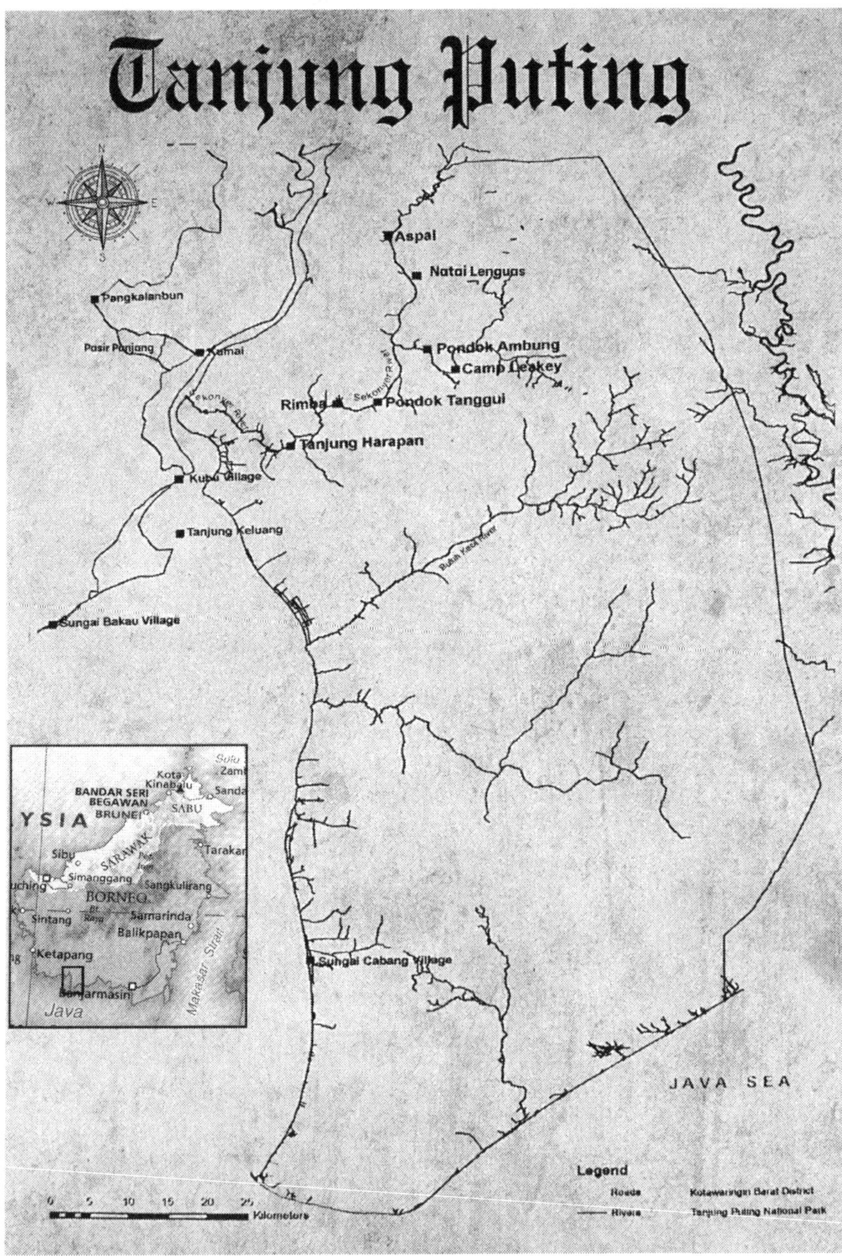

7. Map of Tanjung Puting with points of interest including the relative position of Camp Leakey. The inset shows the relative location of Tanjung Puting on the island of Borneo.

8. The magnificent Sekonyer River in the main channel of this blackwater river system.

9. At the right branch of the Sekonyer River, the blackwater mixes with the main river water.

10. Closer to Camp Leakey, the river narrows with mats of river plants forming "batakan".

11. Aerial view of a seasonal depression lake located downstream from Camp Leakey.

12. A view of the dry seasonal lake area downstream from Camp Leakey.

13. Aerial view of the Aspai gold mines located within the upper watershed of the Sekonyer River.

14. Aerial view of the dock at the river including the ironwood boardwalk and the tower.

15. Aerial view of some of the structures at Camp Leakey that were built on higher ground.

16. Aerial view of the guest house and team house (center top) and longhouse and kitchen area to the right.

17. The guest houses that served as my quarters at Camp Leakey, showing my bedroom, storage room, and toilet.

18. Teaching signs to Rinnie, an adult female orangutan, at the edge of the Sekonyer River.

Orangutan Resentment

Rinnie and I were engaged in something truly ground-breaking for five very important reasons. Firstly, I was teaching an adult great ape how to sign, a feat that had never before been accomplished even within laboratories or other captive settings. Secondly, an orangutan was being taught to sign, a remarkable achievement in and of itself. Thirdly, Rinnie was learning how to sign in her natural environment rather than within a controlled captive setting. Fourthly, Rinnie was free to ignore the study if she wished, which added an element of unpredictability to our interactions. And finally, perhaps most significantly, Rinnie would ultimately return to a life in the wild, rather than being confined in captivity. Let's be clear, great apes, even young ones, are very strong and can be dangerous in close quarters. It is why almost all previous studies have been started with infant or juvenile great apes. To teach Rinnie, I had to sit close to her and manipulate her hands and arms. With her superior strength and grip, Rinnie could have grabbed and hurt me if she had wished. But free-ranging orangutans generally do not act aggressively unless they feel threatened or wronged. And Rinnie was learning to trust me.

Teaching signs to Rinnie was also significant as she was the first orangutan to learn to communicate with signs in a relatively long-term study (twenty-two months). Almost all previous studies have examined the linguistic or signing abilities of chimpanzees (Gardner

& Gardner, 1969; Premack, 1972) or gorillas (Patterson, 1978). Lyn Miles (1993) began teaching nine-month-old Chantek, an orangutan, signs a couple of months after Rinnie's education began. But if orangutans could learn to sign, it would reinforce Gordon Hewes's (1973) "gestural origin of language" hypothesis in that the competency to communicate propositionally with manual gestures (i.e., sign language) might have been established in an earlier pongid/hominid common ancestor rather than a later one (i.e., human/chimpanzee), or appear suddenly and exclusively as a glottogenesis transformation within the hominin lineage leading to modern humans.

Yet five years earlier, I had taught a number of linguistic concepts to a captive Sumatran juvenile orangutan named Aazk over a two-year period within the Fresno (California) City Zoo. It was for my Master's thesis research project at California State University, Fresno. The Gardners (1969) who taught the first signing chimpanzee, Washoe, in fact, suggested I use the artificial symbolic language method of David Premack (1972) rather than their own signing methods because they felt signs would be difficult to train to an orangutan whose hands were adapted to an arboreal life, and of course, being a less social species. I followed their advice and purchased a set of pre-made plastic children's letters and instructed Aazk through matching associations, conditional discrimination, and increasingly complex problem solving to demonstrate her basic linguistic skills. So while Aazk previously showed an orangutan could be taught to use an artificial symbolic communication system (Shapiro, 1975), Rinnie demonstrated her hands were perfectly fine to learn and use signs as well as any other great ape.

The other reason Rinnie's education was significant was that it took place in her own natural environment. Previously, chimpanzees and gorillas had been taught to sign, or to learn symbolic communication, in home-reared or laboratory/captive environments along with other humans who signed or interacted with them behind protective walls (Gardner & Gardner, 1969; Premack & Premack, 1972; Patterson, 1978). Immersion within the human social setting was believed to be the ideal environment for inculcating language. Integrating the young ape into a daily routine of making and eating meals, playing with toys, going to the toilet, while interacting with signing caregivers, as with human children, would provide the most optimal opportunity for the young ape to learn to communicate with signs within the context of their environment. Of course, great apes are not human children, though many psychologists of the day believed in the *tabula rasa* concept and that the mind of the ape could, within its species defined limits, be conditioned to learn behaviors using protocols or contrived apparatuses through observation, imitation, and trial-and-error. But intelligent animals did not evolve in a laboratory. We now know that special learning like imprinting, toxic food avoidance, and species-specific predispositions are evolved features shaped in the unforgiving crucible of the real world (e.g., Lorenz, 1965; Brown, 1975). Would an ape learning to sign in the environment in which its species evolved provide a unique opportunity to ask questions of relevance to its subjective reality and existence? As a zoologist, I thought so and was extremely eager to find out. Would this mean giving up some of the control that psychologists typically strive for within the laboratory setting? Absolutely, but whatever control was lost was made up for in other ways that were well worth the effort.

Unlike other previous ape language studies, Rinnie was free to come and go as she pleased. Perhaps other studies at universities and institutions provide ad lib access to apparatus for the apes to interact with; however, they are under the control of researchers and administrators. Rinnie was free-ranging and would sometimes choose not to come to our sign learning sessions. Her having this control to choose and the freedom to interact with me was one reason she was safe to work with.

Finally, at the end of the twenty-two-month study, Rinnie wasn't retired to a caged environment like so many other great apes. She remained in the local swamp forest across from Camp Leakey for a number of months, then left the area with other orangutans to continue her return to the wild. I never saw her in the following years, but I knew Rinnie was where she was meant to be. Stolen from her mother from the forest as a baby, she was rescued, rehabilitated, and returned to the home of her birthright. Along the way, she was given the opportunity and repeatedly chose to participate in a study that helped humans better understand orangutan cognition.

What of the great apes in other studies? Apart from the publicity, academic success, and popular fame such ape language studies conferred to the apes and the project leadership, the ethical dilemma of disposition of the "subject" at the end of the study has proven to weigh heavily with most all people who have raised or been part of the lives of these special apes (Inggersol and Scarnà, 2023). What could one say to a home-reared Nim (chimpanzee) or Chantek (orangutan) to ease the emotional nose-dive from feeling joyous and important to confused and depressed after being taken, for no fault of their own, from an enriched home life at a college campus to the harsh and cold confines of captivity and incarceration? Rub fist to chest: "Sorry?" No sign or symbol could adequately convey the feelings experienced by all parties to this travesty of fairness in the name of science. This is part of the "moral Frankenstein" we have created in our search for an understanding of great ape cognitive and linguistic ability. In our quest, we have discovered and then stumbled over their sentience. The unfairness of treating a person, like a great ape, in this way comes back to haunt some of us.

Interestingly, captive orangutans do recognize the unfairness of their captivity, remember who wronged them, and express their displeasure or inflict damage to a human if they have a chance at retribution. This implies that they are aware of their own autonomy and the inequity of their incarceration. When teaching symbolic communication to Aazk at the Fresno City Zoo, I would enter her cage before opening hours and spend up to one hour interacting with her, both in play and in the exchange of children's plastic symbols, the medium of communication for the study. While inside the cage she would show affiliative behavior toward me: jump on my lap, hug me, let me swing and tickle her, as well as exchange symbols for food and actions (Shapiro, 1975). Inevitably, I would need to leave the cage once the zoo opened or I had to return to campus. Before leaving the area, I would sometimes spend a few minutes watching her along with the zoo visitors. During those moments of joining the other humans, I repeatedly witnessed her express displeasure at my being outside of her cage where I had left her moments before. She would look at me while I watched her play from outside the enclosure with other visitors, and then she would quickly turn and rush into her night house and stay there until I left the area. One visitor who had watched me prior to my leaving the cage asked me what I did to Aazk that prompted her to spontaneously disappear? In time I came to understand this was Aazk's way of expressing jealousy and resentment for my freedom of movement. I could come and go as I pleased, but she could not. Her expression was directed at me.

I learned about captive orangutan resentment years earlier and had my ribs nearly cracked by an adolescent orangutan named Foots after he grabbed my hand and pulled me against the bars of his enclosure.

I was visiting the orangutans behind the scenes at the Oklahoma City Zoo in 1976 when this happened. It was stupid of me to get so close. I knew it wasn't personal, since Foots had only just met me, but he probably had been harboring feelings of being treated unfairly. I was outside and he was stuck inside. Foots wasn't able to lash out at his keepers, so I was fair game for him to express his displeasure. My hunch is that captive orangutans learn to resent their keepers, not unlike how prison inmates resent their jailers. This isn't to say that some orangutans and keepers don't have good relationships with each other. But we also know that zoo orangutans are known escape artists, talented problem solvers looking for the weak spot in the wire mesh, the loose stones in the wall, or the forgotten water hose left behind by a keeper. They want to get out and explore beyond the walls of even the most naturalistic and stimulating captive environment. Almost all zoos with an orangutan population need to address this challenge.

Rinnie was free-ranging, and I was not a threat to her. In fact, I was bringing food and drink each time I visited. She was not confined to a cage at night, and she was at liberty to join me at our makeshift classroom by the river. After we finished our lessons, she would return to the trees to continue her life as an orangutan. Some days she wouldn't be in the area when I called her name, though most of the time she chose to spend up to one hour or more with me before leaving.

In the days, weeks, and months that followed, Rinnie learned to make dozens of taught signs, invent signs, and combine them in sentence-like utterances (Shapiro & Galdikas, 1999). I would ask her, "What do you want?" in American Sign Language and at the same time, "Apa mau?" in vocal Bahasa Indonesia. And she would respond with: "You, that food, give food," for example. She created the iconic signs "scratch" and "groom" by merely shortening thc actual action of scratching and grooming at the desired location. These action signs were used by her when she felt uneasy or after the food and drink were exhausted and she wanted me to give her contact.

She also comprehended the meaning of a sign. If I signed "give food?" to her and she had an item of low value, she would give it to me to eat, for example, a cassava root. Frequently, her training consisted of my asking her, "What is this?" in sign language and Bahasa Indonesia ("Apa ini?"), and she would have to name an object. Part of my interest was in knowing how many signs an orangutan could learn. For Rinnie, non-food signs were especially uninteresting.

I came to understand that signs were used as "linguistic" tools to get something of value. Food and drink were the priority items of interest for Rinnie, as for all orangutans. I later found that for physical referents (the item whose sign is being taught), orangutan sign learning pace could be predicted by the interest orangutans had in the referent. Because I was the provider of the referent, Rinnie was motivated to learn signs for consumables that she enjoyed as well as signs for grooming, scratching, or brushing. Motivating her to learn signs for referents that were not of interest proved challenging. In some cases, she never learned to produce the correct response to an acceptable criterion even after thousands of trials of training. Her lack of performance to learn signs whose referents were not of interest to her did not jeopardize her from being a "person" in my eyes. She had already proven that early on but a discussion of orangutan personhood provides context beyond her abilities within the sign learning context.

Orangutan Personhood

Scientific research has revealed that great apes share many cognitive, emotional, and social characteristics with humans. This evidence has led many researchers, philosophers, and legal scholars to advocate for granting great apes, including orangutans, legal personhood status Singer (2008), Wise (2006), Andrews (2011), Comstock (2010), Savage-Rumbaugh, & Fields (2000), Tague (2020). While the concept of personhood is often associated with humans, some argue that it should not be limited to our species. I share this view and believe that orangutans should be recognized as legal persons.

My conviction is based not only on theoretical arguments, but also on my personal experience working with and observing orangutans like Rinnie and other orangutans. These animals demonstrate a range of behaviors and capabilities that suggest they should be considered as persons. For instance, their ability to understand the mental states of others (known as theory of mind) and their capacity for self-awareness are cognitive traits that support the case for orangutan personhood.

Theory of mind is a cognitive ability of someone to attribute or infer mental states of oneself and others. It's a higher order ability that appears in human children at about four years of age as well with great apes. To provide examples of Rinnie's theory of mind, I will refer to and quote passages from my 1978-1980 diary that document fascinating instances where I believe Rinnie inferred my state of mind.

The second time I met her (July 5, 1978), I swam across the river and sat down on the riverside log, our first jungle classroom. Rinnie joined me very quickly. I took her hands again and molded the "come" sign several times. I noticed she didn't seem too attentive. Later that afternoon, I visited her again to spend some time with her. I molded the sign for "brush" and then combed her coarse, long hair with my hands. After she and a couple of the other orangutans were fed raw cassava, I took a chunk of the bland root and chewed it to experience how it tasted. It was like a raw potato. Rinnie immediately came up to me and put her face close to my lips. Now she seemed very attentive. I sensed she was begging for the chewed-up carbohydrate and felt compelled to transfer it to her mouth. While I would not do something like that today for health and safety reasons, I wasn't thinking about anything more than satisfying Rinnie's request. At that time, I was establishing a relationship. I spit it into my hand and handed it to her. Surprisingly, she offered a piece of the raw root to me again. Apparently, I was enhancing the value of the root by pre-digesting it and releasing the sugars with my own salivary amylase enzyme. Of course, I complied again.

The next day, I paid another visit to Rinnie. While teaching her the sign for "come," Gundul, a sub-adult male orangutan, arrived at our makeshift classroom. Surprisingly, Gundul did not seem intimidated by my presence. Prior to this encounter, I had heard about Gundul's reputation. In her book "Reflections of Eden" (Galdikas, 1995), Biruté Galdikas described Gundul's sexually aggressive behavior towards one of the Camp cooks years ago. Despite Galdikas's attempts to intervene, Gundul relentlessly pursued the female cook. It is interesting to note that such forced copulation is employed as an

Alternative Reproductive Tactic (Gross, 1996) by wild sub-adult or flangeless male orangutans who are less preferred by adult females compared to cheek-padded adult males. As a result, Gundul was feared by many of the Camp staff. Naturally, I wanted to avoid any physical confrontation with him, especially hand-to-hand combat. Therefore, I swiftly broke off a long root from a nearby waterline tree and held it up as a show of determination, while shouting loudly to indicate that I meant business. In response, Gundul approached, holding a cassava root, occasionally extending it towards me. He sat nearby, about one meter away, as I continued teaching Rinnie the "brush" sign. At one point, she seemed to combine two signs by touching me with an extended finger and then bringing her hand to her head, simulating a comb-like motion. I promptly reinforced her action by actually combing her head, while also consistently emphasizing the correct "brush" sign. Gundul, curious about our activities, moved closer to my hand. Sensing that he might not have friendly intentions, I grabbed the stick and shook it in his direction. This caused him to immediately back away, although he remained observant. After a while, he approached again, prompting me to raise my voice and vigorously wave the stick on the ground, behaving like a madman. Both Gundul and Rinnie were frightened by this, displaying cries, bared teeth, and retreating from the scene. Only when I put the stick down did Rinnie return, while Gundul temporarily left the area. Rinnie and I then continued our work on the "brush" and "come" signs. At one point when she was trying to grab my hand to bring it to her, non-verbally indicating she wanted me to scratch or brush her, I didn't respond. She then grabbed a chunk of cassava root, tore a piece off, and gave it to me. Here was an orangutan trying to reinforce my behavior to pay attention. I was surprised and accepted it, chewed it, and spit it into her mouth. She kept doing this for a while, savoring the partially digested root. When a piece fell on the ground, I washed it in the river before chewing it. Later when I refused another offered piece, Rinnie rinsed it off in the water and presented it again. I had to accept. By this time Gundul had to see what was going on, so he approached from the other side and onto a branch perched over the river. I now knew the taste of raw cassava and had enough of it and Gundul for one day, so I swam back to the Camp side of the river.

From the above account, Rinnie was inferring my state of mind regarding the signing methodology since she was reinforcing my behavior and my attitude about eating dirty cassava when she washed the root after seeing me do the same before eating it. Some could perhaps challenge my interpretation, but I had not trained her to do these behaviors. From my perspective, Rinnie had clearly demonstrated a theory of mind.

Romantic Advances

I occasionally think about the females who have been desirous of me. Not human females. Great ape females. That's right, the vivacious gorilla, lusty chimpanzee, and sultry orangutan. Don't get me wrong, it's not as though there haven't been human females who have been desirous of me. Indeed, there have. However, such a revelation wouldn't be nearly as interesting at first blush.

First, there was Koko the famous signing gorilla who as a youngster expressed a brief interest in me when I visited her in Woodside, California. This was during the time in the early 1970s while I was working with Aazk at the city zoo in Fresno, California, and wanted some insight with another ape language project. Penny Patterson, Koko's main caretaker and sign language teacher invited me to meet and interact with the precocious ape. After a while, Penny said "Koko really liked you." Koko raced around the trailer and came over to me to play a game. It was clearly an adolescent crush. Koko of course continued to have crushes on "strange" human males who visited her, like Robin Williams and Mr. Rogers.

Then when I was in Oklahoma teaching sign language to chimpanzees in the mid-1970s, Washoe the chimpanzee expressed her amorous wishes to me. Washoe was famous as the first ape to learn sign language, and I got to know her while I attended the University of Oklahoma doing my doctoral research at the Institute of Primate Studies. I would sometimes go on casual walks around the back property of the Institute with Washoe and Roger Fouts, my professor and Washoe's caregiver since she was an infant in the 1960s.

During the time I got to know her, Washoe was a young lady with an air of distinction, as if she had the knowledge of her fame in academic circles. After all, language was the unchallenged bastion of human uniqueness before Washoe. Now with a vocabulary of hundreds of signs, Washoe could make her intentions known by gestures as well as non-verbal glances. So, on a sunny morning during the mid-phase of her estrous cycle with her rear end swollen and protruding, Washoe did something surprising. From inside her expanded metal enclosure, she pushed her rear end hard against the sharp-edged fencing toward me and waved her hand beckoning me to come to her. "Hurry, hurry" she would sign. Washoe's turgid red behind would be a major turn-on for an adult male chimpanzee, a physiological signal of her heightened fertility.

Fout's told me later, "Washoe really liked you," but I suspected I wasn't the only human male she propositioned. Remember this was the same chimpanzee who was raised only with human contact during her time at Reno, and who signed, "black bugs" the first time she saw a group of chimpanzees when she came to the institute (Linden, 1974). She had never encountered another chimpanzee before that. Perhaps she saw herself as a human and by extension human males would become appropriate potential mates.

My sweetest of female ape memories came after I arrived at Camp Leakey and started teaching signs to Rinnie. My diary attests to an event that has been published elsewhere, including a British tabloid, and is by far more significant than the two previous stories at demonstrating orangutan personhood:

On July 8, 1978, after bathing at the river, I took the prau across the river to visit Rinnie. We both sat on the classroom log working on "come," "brush," "food" (using cassava), and "drink" (using river water). Surprisingly, she offered me food (cassava) and drink (river water) when I stopped brushing her. Again, she appeared to be reinforcing my behavior with food and drink. Then following our afternoon training session Rinnie took me by the hand and started pulling me as she left the log we both sat on. Her grip was strong and I was surprised, but I was curious as to why she would want to lead me to an unknown location. We walked gingerly, hand-in-hand across the river from Camp, in a dry swamp strewn with mangrove roots and fallen branches.

Then I saw it. A ground nest that Rinnie had built behind a tree. Orangutans make nests out of branches, twigs and leaves, but they normally do it high in the trees. They build fresh ones every evening. But Rinnie made this absolutely beautiful nest with the available branches and leaves collected in the dry swamp.

While still holding my hand, Rinnie got into her nest, laid onto her back, spread her legs, and pulled me toward her.

What did I think? How did I feel? More importantly, what did I do? What I first thought was, "Rinnie wants to have sex with me." I felt surprised and shocked by her forwardness. I was alone with this amorous ape – no one else was in the area to witness the event. After she pulled on my hand a second time, I released my hand from her grip and signed, "No," and walked away.

I later returned to Camp Leakey to process what had just happened. There we no other westerners there to hear my story and perhaps give me their interpretations. I dared not talk to camp staff as my Indonesian was minimal then and what would they think? I was working hard so the staff would respect me as the interim Camp leader. I didn't want to disclose something in my broken Indonesian that might make me look like a twisted westerner at worse or a laughable figure at best.

Years later I came to understand what might have precipitated Rinnie's solicitous behavior. She was an adult orangutan who was raised by humans but then free-ranging. I was a new male, an unusual western male at that, with a beard the color of her own hair, who was bringing special items of food and drink to her, and only her. The other orangutans observed this and were desirous of these treats. Then, as part of the training, I had to manually mold Rinnie's hands into the various configurations that described the sign. I was grooming and brushing her as part of teaching her the signs for those activities. So here I was being so tactile and gentle with her, giving her treats and all this attention in front of other jealous orangutans, also in exile from the Camp Leakey side of the river. Essentially, I was courting her and at the right moment (perhaps a time mid-phase in her cycle) she reciprocated in the only way a confused and aroused adult orangutan might behave: she offered herself to me. Interestingly, the interpretation of my courting Rinnie was pronounced years later by Italian television host, Maurizio Costanzo, when I appeared on his long-running late night television show and gave my account of the incident to a live audience in 1996.

And what fallout did my action cause? Well, you know what they say about a woman scorned. It applies to adult female orangutans as well. For several days after the incident, I sensed coldness in her behavior toward me. She left the training sessions quickly and didn't stay longer for the scratching and brushing once the food and milk ran out. But that didn't last for long. And on my birthday, August 8, Rinnie following the training portion of the session, would sign, "you groom", "you scratch" pointing to specific areas of her body where she wanted me to attend to her. Most of the time she would like to hold my hand while lying back and make deep throaty sounds through her throat pouch during exhalation. Since orangutans have 28-day menstrual cycles, I now infer she was probably proceptive during both of these times. But what a birthday present.

When Galdikas heard about the incident months later, Rinnie was back to her old self, but Galdikas merely said, "You should have done it for science." Was she joking? Half joking?

I countered with the quip, "It wouldn't be right bedding your student." I did have to keep the relationship somewhat formal. And what would the Vatican say? It was bad enough I was teaching orangutans "language" and possibly inculcating a soul, as the local German-born Catholic Pastor Moher would say. We really didn't need to add to the controversy the possible sexual union with the apes.

Of course, sexually active male orangutans have been known to force themselves on females: orangutan and human females. This has been reported by Galdikas and others and appears to be a sexual strategy of subadult or flangeless males (though cheek padder males have been known to forcibly copulate with adult female orangutans). The male orangutan's penis is not a visually impressive organ. It is short (three inches) and narrow, made erect by the os bacculum or penis bone. It has evolved as one would surmise to be accommodated within the female orangutan's genitalia. It could, physically, be accommodated by a human female, though it is unclear if such forcible efforts reported by Galdikas in the case of the Camp Leakey cook, was effective, i.e., actual penetration, or merely (not to diminish the fear experienced) being forcibly held by four gripping hands and feet, and some thrusting against clothing.

Let me return to the moment after I refused Rinnie's advance. While she was perhaps feeling rejected by me, she did something that was notable within a "theory of mind" interpretation. When I was ready to leave Rinnie for the day, after our encounter, a four-year-old male orangutan kept getting into the prau, wanting a trip to the Camp. I said "no" in Indonesian and had to physically use the oar to push him out. Rinnie, surprisingly, assisted me by pulling on the orangutan as I pushed. Apparently, she perceived my irritation and helped me out. She gave a small bite to the young male orangutan afterward.

In addition to building a ground nest and offering herself to me, perhaps by presuming I was interested in a more serious relationship, Rinnie inferred my state of mind by offering me food and drink to influence my providing her with contact, and by helping me get the young orangutan out of the boat so I could get back to Camp. There could be other explanations for why Rinnie acted as she did (redirected aggression due to her frustration?). Yet, her behaviors were consistent with those that imply a theory of mind in a great ape.

A Perception of Fairness and Inequity

Frans de Waal and Sarah Brosnan (2003) demonstrated social inequity aversion in a study called "Monkeys Reject Unequal Pay" when a capuchin monkey is given a lower value reward as compared to another monkey in view who receives a higher value reward for the same previous performance. In a fascinating video of this behavior (search YouTube with "two monkeys were paid unequally"), the monkey who received a piece of cucumber for a reward becomes visibly frustrated and throws it back at the experimenter (aversion) after seeing the other monkey receive a sweet grape for the same work. Such frustration doesn't occur when both monkeys receive a piece of cucumber for the same performance. It is the perceived inequity that elicits the response.

Brosnan, et al. (2004) also demonstrated inequity aversion with chimpanzees though they showed that tolerance for inequity was a function of social closeness of individuals in the group. As a social species, it would follow that a closely related individual or one with a close affiliation would not be as dissatisfied by that relative or friend's receiving a disproportionately more valuable reward than herself.

Interestingly, Brosnan, et al. (2011) found that socially housed orangutans did not demonstrate inequity aversion as did the more social capuchin monkeys and chimpanzees and suggested that inequity responses are a convergent behavior based on either sociality or cooperative tendency. As orangutans are considered the least social primates, their failure to demonstrate inequity aversion could be explained away simply by an individual orangutan's inability to recognize he was being shortchanged. It could also be that orangutans do not feel cheated when a cage-mate receives a higher valued reward within the performance/reward paradigm. Expressing displeasure at receiving something of lesser value for the same amount of work doesn't seem to resonate with orangutans, a species that generally does not cooperate in social problem-solving in the wild. Interestingly, however, orangutans do express their displeasure when they personally experience being directly cheated or wronged by an individual, and they will take action to exact revenge even long after the event of inequity.

For example, when I was at Camp Leakey in 1978-1980, I recall Usman complaining about his feud with a particular free-ranging orangutan, Sobiarso. Sobiarso was one of the adolescent female orangutans who spent most of her time around Camp Leakey. She was very inquisitive and liked to amble into the staff's quarters from time to time. Usman did not take kindly to this and would occasionally punish Sobiarso by locking her in a cage. As a result, Sobiarso formed a particular dislike of Usman and for many months would take revenge by targeting and destroying the fruits of his labor or items valued by Usman. In one instance, Usman spent hours repairing the camp generator. The repair required the proper placement of cables and wires from the generator as well as a fuel line to the diesel engine powering the machine. Sobiarso took notice of Usman's dedication and efforts to restore the source of the Camp's meager electricity. After fixing the system, Usman locked the generator shed and headed to the river to bathe. Apparently, Sobiarso managed to break into the shed while Usman and other Camp workers were at the river. When Usman returned to turn on the electricity for the evening, he found all his work was ruined. Wires were torn loose and the fuel line was pulled off.

In another instance of apparent revenge, Sobiarso broke into the sleeping quarters of Usman. Now, normally orangutans who break into human housing seek out tins of food and bottles of drink and us humans at Camp Leakey know this, which is why the effort is always made to keep doors locked and windows covered by chain-link screening, but Sobiarso wasn't interested in Usman's food. Rather, she proceeded to destroy a small shrine he had constructed on his bookshelf displaying photographs and memorabilia of his girlfriend Diana back in Java. Materials were scattered on the floor and some photographs and personal letters were removed and found later outside. Sobiarso understood this shrine was of value to Usman. Apparently, this act of retribution wasn't enough to even the score. Sobiarso repeated this violation of Usman's sacred shrine one more time weeks later before she finally let her grudge go.

I personally experienced the pain of retribution given to me by an orangutan whom I very much liked and respected. It happened in the late 1980s during an Earthwatch expedition. Camp Leakey was hosting nearly a dozen tourists on a "working vacation" as a way to generate funds. I had been visiting Camp Leakey at the time and was planning to do a dive in Bali after the trip.

The orangutan was named Siswoyo, an ex-captive, adult female whom I first met a decade earlier. She was six and a half months pregnant when I encountered her while heading for breakfast. As I wrote in my diary for July 6, 1978, "she (Siswoyo) took a liking to me and immediately climbed on my shoulders and back for a ride (she weighs about 30 kilograms). Apparently, she did some damage to the dining hall in the night, though I was told she was a pretty good-natured gal." She was even tempered, and I had developed a close and trusting relationship with her during the first two years at Camp Leakey.

But during my visit in the late 1980s, I was giving an informal demonstration about orangutan intelligence to two of the Earthwatch volunteers. Both were nurses from the United States. Siswoyo happened to be behind the team house digging in the soil for clay. Siswoyo did that from time to time, perhaps addressing a mineral deficiency she might have had. I knew she was a good tool user so I gave Siswoyo my pocketknife with one of the large blades out. She took the knife and started using it appropriately as a digging implement. I explained to the two nurses, "Orangutans can make use of human implements to solve problems on their own. Just watch Siswoyo." She kept digging and scraping with the knife. But then she started putting the blade into her mouth to taste the dirt and clay. I started to worry that she might cut her lips or mouth with the sharp blade, so I asked her to give it back to me in Indonesian. Of course, she just ignored my request. So I proceeded to show the nurses just how smart I was, a big mistake. I said to Siswoyo in English, "Sis, look over there!" Pointing to a tree somewhere in the distance. Siswoyo turned to look in that direction, and while she was distracted, I quickly pulled the knife from her hand. Real smart human, right? I felt relieved that Siswoyo was safe again. She didn't appear upset and continued to sit next to me. I proceeded to explain to the two nurses that orangutans were capable of learning sign language and that I could demonstrate the technique with Siswoyo. I grabbed her hands and said, "The first thing you need to do is to mold the hands..." and as I continued to finish my sentence, Siswoyo grabbed my hands like a steel vise and slowly brought them toward her mouth. I tried pulling them free but could not.

Like a slow-moving wreck, I watched helplessly while Siswoyo put my hand into her mouth and punctured the back of my hand right below my ring finger with one of her large canine teeth. When she was done, she let my hand go and left the area.

The two nurses asked me if I was okay. We looked at the clean hole that went to the tendons. I could watch my tendons move as I wiggled the finger. So no nerve damage. Then one of the nurses said, "You look white, I think you are going into shock." Fortunately, I was in good care as they washed the wound with antiseptic and covered it with gauze. All I could think about was, no diving in Bali this year.

Following the incident, I came to realize the errors I made that led to my being bitten. It was completely my fault and avoidable: 1. I shouldn't have given Siswoyo a pocketknife to demonstrate her tool-using ability; 2. I tricked Siswoyo. I reneged on the gift when I should have traded her with something of higher value to get the knife back; and 3. I stood too close to an orangutan who was wronged and paid the price.

In retrospect, we see that orangutans can inhibit their displeasure and wait for the right time to exact their revenge. This implies deception of their true motivation and temporal displacement. Siswoyo also measured her response by giving me what I affectionately call a "love bite." She could have done more damage to me. I learned an important lesson: it doesn't pay to trick an orangutan, and I truly believe she liked me and only wanted to punish me in a proportional way for my bad behavior. Siswoyo passed away in 1991, but I will always remember her as an orangutan person of dignity who taught me that important lesson regarding human arrogance and an orangutan's response of being tricked, particularly in light of their strength.

Out of the Cage: Princess

"Princess is a genius" is a phrase I have heard many times by people who have watched this special "person" over the years, particularly in the recent past when I wasn't in Central Borneo where she made her home. Princess was my adopted orangutan daughter. Let me make that clear, the adoption was mutual of course, since she leaped out of her holding enclosure into my arms, and I graciously accepted her as my student and my "child." That was the way it was for me in 1978. She was around four years of age, and I was a divorced twenty-seven-year-old graduate student who never had a child at that point. She should have been with her natural orangutan mother, but she was rescued and brought to Camp Leakey for rehabilitation, the term used at the time – now it is reintroduction.

Princess was my first child. She was with me for nearly two years while I taught her sign language in the middle of a Bornean rainforest. She lived with me in the guest house at Camp Leakey, slept in the same bed much of the time, had her meals with me in the morning and afternoon, clung to me as I traveled around Camp Leakey, and played in the trees with other young orangutans when I visited Rinnie across the river. These were opportunities to learn and use signs. While she learned signs, I learned much about being a dad.

As I demonstrated in my 1982 publication, Princess learned to make some thirty-seven signs within a nineteen-month time frame. She was as capable as Washoe, a chimpanzee and the first signing great ape, and as Koko, the famous signing gorilla. Princess could also combine signs into what could be called sentences to ask for items and activities of interest ("you scratch there"), or to report new items ("sweet fruit" to describe canned pineapple). Princess, an orangutan, thus proceeded into the pantheon of precocious propositionally communicating primates to take her place alongside chimpanzees, gorillas, bonobos, and billions of humans.

What's more, Princess and other orangutans who became my students not only learned to express themselves with signs in their native habitat, the rainforest, but they also returned to the rainforest at the end of the studies as normal, free-ranging, and proud primates, something that could not be said of any other great ape in a sign language study.

We humans are very good at using our superior brainpower to dominate and control life on this planet. We are not so good at caring for the long-term survival of such life, as evidenced by how we are decimating habitats, species, and cooking our own biosphere. We also have very little regard for animals we don't keep as our household pets, as evidenced by the annual slaughter of billions of factory-farmed animals to put nonhuman flesh on our dinner plates.

Great apes come to know who they are as evidenced by their self-awareness, their "theory of mind," and other cognitive abilities. These capacities, according to many cited throughout this book, give them "personhood" status. As great ape-persons, these individuals understand they have gone from feeling loved as special youngsters, pleasing the scientists and giving them what they so desperately want, to being limited, constrained, and denied the freedom that they remember and still want. These accounts shed light on a deeply troubling aspect of our treatment of great apes: the tendency to perceive them as mere objects rather than individuals deserving of respect and agency. Their profound cognitive capacities and understanding of their own existence challenge our preconceived notions and force us to confront the ethical implications of our interactions with them. Princess may not have been as famous as Chantek (Miles, 1993), but she was set free like Rinnie and lived a rich and full life as an orangutan. This means that Princess actively participated in sustaining her ecosystem habitat. Along the way, she raised five offspring, contributed something to our understanding of orangutan cognition, intelligence, and behavioral ability, and amazed and surprised us.

Anne Russon (2004) came to know Princess when she was studying orangutan intelligence. Princess became a skilled toolmaker and tool user. She had observed the humans at Camp Leakey over the decades using tools like saws, hammers, screwdrivers, pens, and pencils, as well as keys, toothbrushes, scrub brushes, rags, oars, and she learned to use them all. She also made sponges, mouth protectors, primitive keys, levers, scrapers, and shovels. Life at Camp Leakey provided a rich opportunity for an inquisitive orangutan like Princess to observe, play, experiment, and engage in activities required to use and make tools, things Princess's wild peers in Borneo do not have in abundance.

The first time I saw Princess, on July 3, 1978, she was one of about nine juvenile orangutans in a safety enclosure near the forestry department building at Camp Leakey. It was my first complete day at Camp, and so I didn't know her name then. The staff was giving out reconstituted powdered milk. I visited the enclosure each day to check on the health of the orangutans and noticed she was the smallest of all the youngsters, kept there to protect them from the pythons and wild pigs that roamed the area. On July 8, I took data on Princess's behavior, but she made it difficult as she kept clinging to the chain-link and watching me.

Then about a month later, on August 3, I took Princess out of her safety enclosure for a trek into the nearby swamp forest. She rode on my back and shoulders, clinging to my red beard and clutching my shirt firmly. I knew an orangutan at this age would normally be climbing trees with her mother, but Princess was an orphan. So, I placed her on a small pole-like tree, and she climbed up, but she was reluctant to come down. For the next thirty minutes, Princess threw a tantrum as she was clearly afraid. She hadn't spent a lot of time in the trees due to her life in captivity and later at Camp Leakey, maintained in a safety enclosure. Eventually, Princess was able to transfer to another adjacent and larger tree, but she kept screaming. In the wild, the mother would come to the baby's rescue. I called her name and beckoned for her to come down. Princess just kept circling the tree trunk screaming and defecating. I felt sorry for Princess and remembered being a bit worried she might fall. But orangutans would be extinct if they lost their grip while crying in a highly emotional state. Finally, exhausted, she shimmied down the trunk of the tree, much like a bear cub, rear-end first, until she could grab onto me. Once in my arms, she did not want to let go. She clung to me tightly as I returned to Camp and placed her in the enclosure with her peers.

The following day, I climbed inside the safety enclosure with the nine young orangutans. What a sight. I sat down and while almost all the orangutans seemed curious, Princess immediately came over and clung to me. Her cuddling of me seemed to irritate a young male orangutan who threw a tantrum, perhaps jealous of my giving comfort or perhaps taking his favorite cage-mate away from him. Most of these orangutans were traumatized and showed a continual psychological need for comfort. Most would either cling to another cage-mate or cling to themselves, self-medicating in an attempt to satisfy their primate need for that essential nutrient of love. Psychologist Harry Harlow (1958;1965) demonstrated this necessity when he deprived young monkeys of their mother and showed that warm and fuzzy replicas of their mother were more effective in creating a normal monkey than a sterile wireframe replica. Princess found her mother figure with me. But in the cage, another wide-eyed male juvenile did not. He did not cling to another orangutan either. He seemed content to be by himself as would a normal adolescent, demonstrating that orangutans are as different as humans.

After conducting a battery of tests on the young orangutans in my dissertation study, I found that Princess preferred to use her left hand in solving problems of dexterity. Many of the other orangutans preferred to use their right hand. While each individual orangutan seemed to have a bias in using one or the other hand in such tasks, the orangutan population as a whole does not demonstrate a right-handed bias as in the human population. One of the advantages of working at Camp Leakey in the late 1970s was that there was a sizeable population of young ex-captive orangutans. This was an opportunity to better understand the species rather than a single individual, and to compare sign learning performance of four orangutans to that of four chimpanzees (Fouts, 1972). Because of her affection toward me, Princess was assigned to be the home-reared group.

When I opened the door of the safety enclosure on October 11, 1978, she literally leaped into my arms to begin our special relationship. I immediately started sign training and collecting data. When it came time to work with Rinnie, I took Princess across the river and she clung to me while I interacted with Rinnie. Before putting her to bed, we had an early dinner outside where sign training continued. Three days later, we started the special ten-sign study with the four orangutans. On the same day, Princess made her first unprompted sign for "food." Later that day, she joined me for a swim in the river, riding on my shoulders and neck.

Princess was learning to sign not only in the formal ten-sign study, but throughout the day in the more informal environment analogous to that of young Washoe and Koko. Princess was in direct contact with me, and she had the choice of playing with other orangutans when she wasn't in her signing lessons. But she was initially having a difficult time when I gave her to the Indonesian students to either keep an eye on her temporarily or when the students conducted sign training with her. She would throw a tantrum and cry horribly until she was tired out or I came back to claim her.

Princess was treating me like her mother, especially when she clung to me. She expressed her jealousy and need for my attention if I spent time with other orangutans at Camp Leakey. When I brought her across the river with me to teach Rinnie, as I note in my diary entry of October 18, 1978, she would try to keep me from interacting with Rinnie. Princess would either pull my hand away from her or quickly lean toward Rinnie and try to bite her hand. When I had to go to town, I would reluctantly give her to the Indonesian students who were at Camp Leakey conducting their own research. They would watch Princess while I went away or worked with Rinnie. The first time I returned from town in early November after only two days of separation, Princess appeared temporarily cold toward me.

I would encourage Princess to interact with the various referents that were used to teach signs at home. I was careful not to teach her signs that were employed exclusively in the formal ten-sign study, so as to not give her an unfair advantage. As each trial was recorded, measuring effort and performance was important in determining how quickly a sign was learned according to specific criteria. As Princess played with items under my watchful eye, I was emulating what her mother would be doing, though I was much more liberal and tolerant of her explorative behavior. Her education with me as her teacher and parent facilitated her becoming highly inquisitive and inventive. On one occasion, the combination of my lack of attentiveness and her curiosity, almost cost Princess her life.

A Day to Forget

That is the title to my diary entry for December 21, 1978, the day Princess poisoned herself by drinking kerosene from a plastic container kept behind my bed. Orangutans must think that containers hold tasty liquids, but they learn the hard way that some fluids are not so good to drink. I also learned the hard way that a responsible parent looks out for their child.

The day started out rather early, at 5:30 a.m.. She got up and wanted to play. We did some sign training. I took Princess to the longhouse for her special session training with Pola. Afterwards, I tried operating on Pola's foot which had an open wound perhaps due to a pig bite. We had no catgut for stitching up wounds and the regular thread I used wasn't strong enough to close the gash. I was feeling really depressed to see Pola suffer as he did. I had to take a break and went to bathe at the small lakes that formed near the boardwalk during the rainy season. I frequently went to the river when I was feeling down. I decided not to work with Rinnie that day because of how I was feeling. I didn't want to take that negative emotion with me, as I realized I could have soured the session with Rinnie if I continued to think about how bad I felt.

When I got back to camp and found Princess playing, I took her home. She was still in a playful and explorative mood, a real handful. I let her have the run of the house for a bit while I was looking over some data and playing some music to cheer myself up in the main room of the guest house. All of a sudden, I heard loud and unusual moaning from the other room. I rushed in and saw how Princess's facial expressions made it look like she was clearly in pain. I saw an opened and spilled jug of kerosene.

I immediately grabbed Princess and ran carrying her to the dining hall where some of the crew and I forced her to drink copious amounts of water through a hose. I knew enough not to get her to vomit as aspirating hydrocarbons like kerosene could cause damage to the lungs. Princess was defecating diarrhea everywhere as we worked to dilute the kerosene in her system. And despite her protestations, we continued to work on her.

I wasn't going to let my orangutan daughter die of kerosene poisoning.

I took her back to the guest house and watched over her. As worried as I was, I felt somewhat relieved that she wasn't making the pained facial contortions anymore. Soon Princess fell asleep in her own room, yet despite my relief about Princess, I still felt depressed about what had happened. After taking a quick cool bath, I went to Rod's place to read Merck's Manual about hydrocarbon poisoning and then gathered some food at the dining hall for Princess to eat once she awoke.

Being this close to losing your child, human or nonhuman, by accidental poisoning reminded me of how dangerous life is, especially during the naive early years. Normally, an orangutan mother would show her child what to eat and what not to eat. There are a lot of toxic plants in the forest. But Princess was being home-reared by me, and as a curious orangutan, she loved to explore and look for new things to consume. Was home-rearing and teaching signs to Princess shifting her world view from a more conservative perspective seen in wild orangutans to a more liberal attitude, with greater risks and benefits as the consequence? As a twenty-seven-year-old surrogate dad, was I negligent in not paying attention to her local environment? I just wasn't sure anymore.

After about a half hour, I returned to the guest house to check in on her. When she awoke a few minutes later, I tried feeding her. Princess took a few bites of rice and broth, something soft and nourishing for her empty stomach. When I asked her what she wanted in sign language, she was understandably silent. She was still tired and worn out from the day's ordeal, so I put her back in her room and stayed with her in her bed comforting her until she went to sleep.

Once she was deep asleep, I left Princess, changed my clothes and went to the dining hall to talk and have dinner with the crew. Later in the evening, I did something unusual. I brought out a slide projector, set it up in the dining hall, and showed some of Rod's slides of the crew to themselves. This helped me temporarily take my mind off of Princess and her suffering. They seemed to enjoy seeing their images on the wall of the dining hall. This stressful day ended with me reading and writing at Rod's house, then going home to check on Princess and head off to sleep myself. When I opened the door to her room, I was relieved she was breathing normally and still sleeping comfortably.

The following day, Princess appeared to be feeling much better. She did her signing lessons including some early morning signs, her sign acquisition, and special session training with Pola. We later went to the small lake near the boardwalk for a quick bath then home to rest. Princess was still subdued in her behavior - clearly not in a rambunctious mood. But she seemed like she was on the mend and I felt she could be left for a longer period so I could return to my other projects. So, I let Dolah watch Princess while I went to work with Rinnie. Later I gathered my other data books and training items to conduct the special sessions with my other orangutan students: Rantai and Hampas. After the rain forced us to finish those lessons inside the PPA building, I grabbed some rice and vegetables for Princess, collected her from Dolah and took her home. While not 100%, she was tolerant of some informal signing while I fed and hugged her. Then, without being fussy, allowed me to put her to bed for the night.

While Princess seemed to feel better, I had more excitement in store that evening. First, when I arrived at the dining hall, I found that both Siswoyo and Binti Orangutan were on the roof of the dining hall ripping out shingles, so I literally climbed up in the dark to chase them down. Later, as I was preparing to go to Rod's place to read, the house key was nowhere to be found. I spent the next hour frantically looking around the camp, backtracking my steps for that key to no avail. I asked staff about it. Nothing. I eventually gave up searching by flashlight, hoping the morning light would make finding the key easier.

On the day before Christmas Eve, I was up at 7 a.m. with Princess, still not completely well, looking for the key to Rod's place, which had gone missing the night prior, perhaps stolen or accidentally dropped? I had just entered the kitchen, a place orangutans' sometimes break into, with Princess, and she made a sickening mess defecating diarrhea all over the kitchen entrance. Not only had I still not found the key, but I also had to clean up her foul mess! I wanted to cry but actually screamed out in disgust.

After calming down, I kept looking for the damned key with no success. I had Tumin, a young camp worker who was adopted into the Dayak community, watch Princess while student Mudji and I collected sign acquisition data. Missing key or not, my research had to continue. As the other male crew prepared to leave Camp to monitor the botanical plots in the study area, Tumin announced, "Saya ketemu kunci!" translated: "I found the key!" Everyone had a big laugh, and it seemed I was the last to know.

But, I was now relieved I could access the resources in Birute and Rod's house without having to break in myself and replace the lock.

Just when I thought the day could only get better from there, three other staff members, Dolah, Muspah, and Ernah, wanted to head downstream. More headaches. I tried to find out why, and it seemed that Dolah was unhappy with his wife, Muspah, for not working hard enough. Dolah walked away in a huff, so while I sat with Mudji, one of the Indonesian students, Ernah, chased after him. Things seemed to calm down a bit with Dolah, but he could be mercurial. I later tried talking with him about young wives (Muspah was only fourteen years old) and the importance of patience, before going to special session to work with Hampas and Rantai. Dolah said he would watch Princess and Pola while Mudji and I conducted the lessons.

After working with the two caged students, I returned to Rod's place to examine Pola's feces with the microscope. He was still infested with the ciliate parasite *Balantidium coli* from something foul he must have ingested and was given tetracycline for treatment.

Later, I headed to the dining hall to cook silica gel (a desiccant for keeping instruments and cameras dry inside cases) and to prepare for Rinnie. Ernah, camp cook and housekeeper, agreed to watch Princess while I worked with Rinnie.

After walking the two hundred meters to the river, I couldn't see the good prau near the platform. So, I waded into the swampy part of the small lakes in search of the prau with no luck. I did find our leaky dugout canoe, and took it to the feeding station. As I rounded the bend going into the small channel to the feeding station, I saw the good prau nearby. Apparently, Rio, the oversized adolescent orangutan, stole it and brought it over with the fragrant but fibrous pandanus fruit inside.

Male Dispersion

Camp Leakey had and still has a resident population of ex-captive, free-ranging orangutans and the free-ranging offspring of ex-captive orangutans. The numbers have changed over the years since Camp Leakey's founding and an interesting pattern has emerged. The long-lasting residents are female orangutans while the males eventually leave, sometimes for a while, usually for good, sometimes on their own, and occasionally by force.

It's a dynamic that is consistent with the way wild populations disperse from their natal group, i.e., mother and offspring. One of the genders needs to disperse to avoid the real long-term problem of genetic inbreeding.

We all know about the problem of inbreeding within human subpopulations. For example, historically when royalty allowed for cousins and close relatives to marry, offspring would usually express characteristics that would lead to a loss of vigor or manifestation of diseases, such as hemophilia. These may be the result of an offspring who received the deleterious gene from both parents. If the two are closely related, there is a higher probability of the offspring getting two doses of the deleterious genes.

This can also happen in nonhuman animals, so there are mechanisms that have evolved to prevent close relatives from breeding. There is incest taboo (i.e., avoidance of sexual behavior between brothers and sisters, parents and offspring) and dispersal mechanisms (i.e., one gender leaving the natal group upon reaching sexual maturity). In the case of chimpanzees, it is the female who leaves the community to be taken into a neighboring community of less related male chimps. For orangutans, it is the male who disperses from the "family" group, which is the mother and dependent young. Daughters set up home ranges next to or near their mother's home range. As males become sexually mature, but before their cheek pads or flanges fully develop, they leave their mother's home range and begin wandering into more distant forests where they attempt to breed with unrelated female orangutans. Adult females typically will protest the advances of these flangeless males (also called sub-adult males). Some have called this a form of rape, but it is perhaps better to call it "forced copulation." The flangeless males become more aggressive in their courtship tactics (as they are undesirable by the adult females) and in the case of the ex-captive population of orangutans at Camp Leakey, on almost all occasions, these males eventually become such a problem that they are moved out of Camp or they wander off on their own.

Princess Theory of Mind

When Princess was approximately six years old, she finally got one over on me. It was getting late in the day on March 28, 1980. After playing with some of the other ex-captive orangutans, including Unyuk, Rombe, and Siswoyo in the grassy area under the observation tower near the river, Princess and I returned to our home. As soon as we entered the door, Princess rushed into my room and hopped onto my bed. It was clearly bedtime for Princess. Other orangutans had already built their nests in preparation for sleep. By this time, she had her own room, but I let her stay and fall asleep in my bed. As usual, I would lie down with her until she was sleeping and then get up to get dinner. When I returned home to work for a while by lamplight, Princess was still sleeping soundly. After I completed my work, I crawled back to bed, trying not to wake her. At 1:30 a.m., she woke me, so I picked her up and put her into another bed in a spare guest room. She protested by crying and rushed back into my bed. Tired and not in the mood for her to throw a tantrum, I let her sleep in my bed once again. I was the one to sleep in the spare guest room. Several minutes later I heard a noise in my room and upon checking, I found that Princess had opened and spilled my contact lens solution on my bed. She obviously tried drinking the saline solution. Seeing I was not happy, she put up no fuss when I took her to her own room for the rest of the evening. I went back to the spare bedroom rather than sleep on a wet mattress. Princess was aware of my mood and my level of tolerance. She used this knowledge to position herself close to potential resources, but she also knew enough not to push her luck when she was caught taking the contact lens solution. She inhibited her emotions and called it a night.

On numerous occasions, Princess demonstrated her tool-using intellect in the most innovative ways. In late November 1979, I found Princess playing under my bed. Upon closer inspection, I observed her manipulating a bloated terrestrial leech. Her discovery of this leech answered my own question as to why my legs were bleeding that morning. Apparently, the leech climbed into my bed during the night, took its blood meal, and fell off once satisfied, then Princess noticed it. She did not touch the leech directly. Instead, she took the hem of my bed's mosquito net and used it to wrap the leech after which she rolled and smashed it on the wooden floor. She picked up the bloody, rolled-up netting and bit the leech. Shortly, she lost interest and left the area. What was significant in this episode is how Princess repurposed available material to serve as an insulator. I observed her on another occasion pick up a plastic wrapper and use it to insulate her teeth from directly contacting a chunk of ice before biting it. This ability to solve a problem without apparent trial and error was an indication of Princess's intelligence.

As she grew older, Princess watched other orangutans steal canoes, and she became very good at taking them for rides across the river on her own. Even the intentional sinking of the boats in the shallows near Camp Leakey by staff to prevent orangutan theft did not dissuade Princess. She learned to imitate the staff's technique of bringing the canoe back into service, something requiring a series of steps including raising the boat, moving it forward and backward to eject water, then rocking the boat sideways to bail more water until it was able to float. She would then get into the boat and use her hands as paddles to ferry herself across the river or to forage on the vegetation along the river. Such boat stealing behavior has become part of the Camp Leakey orangutan culture. Other orangutans have learned by observation and have become skilled at stealing unattended speedboats as well as sunken canoes. Through watching their mother, Princess's own offspring have acquired the skills, thereby passing down "boat stealing" as an intergenerational behavior or proto-culture.

Princess also demonstrated tool-making behavior when she would fashion pieces of wood or sticks into primitive keys to pick the sliding lock at Camp Leakey's dining hall. Free-ranging orangutans would occasionally sneak into the washroom adjacent to the dining hall where trash or old rice was temporarily stored. This was possible when staff did not pay attention to the door and forgot to lock it. However, Princess was one of the first orangutans to learn to take old shingles made of ironwood and break off pieces along the grain that would be narrow enough to slip into the sliding door lock. She became very good at picking the lock to gain access to the kitchen. Such tool-making skills would be on par with the orangutans of Suaq Belimbing in Sumatra who fashion dipping sticks to forage for insects and honey.

Tool-making among Bornean orangutans has been said to pale in comparison to the Sumatran orangutan. Orangutans in Borneo make tools out of branches to scratch their backsides while Sumatran orangutans make tools to extract foods that are encased or otherwise hard to access. Ian Singleton, orangutan researcher and conservationist who has worked in Sumatra for more than two decades, boldly asserts in various places that Sumatran orangutans are smarter than their Bornean cousins. While examples of tool making among wild Bornean orangutans are admittedly not that impressive, captive and ex-captives from both islands have shown tool-making skills on par with wild chimpanzees, suggesting that all great apes have the competence to be tool makers and users but lack the environmental and psychological opportunities to express their abilities. We can look at sign learning and signing behavior as a form of tool-making and tool-using. Using symbols to obtain items or activities of interest, Princess was given those opportunities to make and use symbolic tools which unleashed her intellect to solve problems outside the signing context. In addition, she had the opportunities to play at Camp Leakey and to experiment with various objects. As shown by Damerius , et al. (2017), Princess's tool-making and using performance was enhanced by a cascade of factors including a reduction in neophobia and an increase in curiosity, exploration, and problem-solving.

Planning ahead and deception are abilities generally considered to require a higher intellect. In the first case, projecting oneself mentally into the future rather than reacting or responding in the moment suggests neurological and psychological competence to plan. We now know that adult male orangutans point their evening long calls in the direction they plan to travel the following day (van Schaik, et al. 2013). Inhibiting information or giving false information (prevarication) also requires neurological and psychological competence to deceive. Princess was also highly skilled in planning ahead and in deceiving others to obtain items of interest. Russon (2004a, p. 87) recounts Princess's interactions with volunteers helping at Camp Leakey in the early 1990s. Princess and her infant daughter, Peta, were on the porch of the visitor team house interacting with the new volunteers. After a while, she left the area by effortlessly scrambling up the side of the two-story building, with hands and feet. Once she reached the roof, she stayed only a moment, which was unusual for an orangutan, and came back down to the porch of the team house to spend time with the visitors. Instead of leaving for the feeding area at 4:00 p.m., she stayed and actually went to sleep on the porch as dusk approached. When the dinner bell rang at about 8:00 p.m. that evening, Princess was still sleeping on the porch in front of the door. Each visitor leaving the team house stepped over Princess, and the last person locked the door.

When the humans came back a couple of hours later, Princess and Peta were gone. Many thought she had left to build an arboreal nest nearby, despite the late hour. After the door was unlocked, it wouldn't move. A sliding lock on the inside had kept the door secured, and a light shining through the screened window revealed Princess and Peta sitting quietly on the floor. One of the visitors who had been to Camp Leakey before asked Princess, in Bahasa Indonesian, to open the door. She complied, and together Princess and Peta left the house, calmly passing the visitors.

Upon inspection, they found that Princess had made a bit of a mess upstairs where she gained entrance through a hole near the rooftop. A bottle of Pepto-Bismol was poured into a can of Gatorade, classic experimentation by Princess. Significantly, Princess was able to inhibit her immediate motivation to enter the team house earlier in the day when she first spotted the hole near the roof. She understood that humans would not take kindly to her breaking in when they were nearby. She formed a plan to gain entrance once the humans had left for dinner, something that required patience and a preconceived pattern of action.

I will end the list of examples of what I suggest provides evidence of orangutan personhood and agency with another anecdote from one of my many visits with Princess as an adult. In the early 2000s, I visited Camp Leakey with friends and family. As in previous visits, I would call out her name, "Princess," and let her know in the Indonesian language I was at Camp, "Papa disini." My visits to Camp Leakey were only for a few hours at a time by then, and there was no guarantee I would find her as she could be in the forest when the wild fruits were plentiful. After searching for several minutes, Princess and her new dependent son, Percy, appeared. Princess, with Percy attached to her side, came toward me and sat down right in front of me, perhaps waiting for me to start signing to her as I did decades before. Orangutans, like Princess, do not forget specific, personal relationships they have formed or what they have learned, though they may become rusty in how they express themselves.

I signed to her, "Apa mau?" or "What do you want?" Immediately, she took my hand and led me to the old guest house where we lived years before. She pulled me onto the porch and in front of a locked door. She then tapped on the door, grabbed my hands, and moved them to the door handle. She was, in no uncertain terms, asking me to open the door. Behind the door, I was to learn, were bananas. Her tapping on the door was a poor version of the sign "open" she learned decades before. She clearly had forgotten the proper hand movements but I understood what she meant. I signed to her, "No, I can't," but Princess would not have any of it. She repeated this several times, and each time I signed, "No, I can't." Eventually we both walked away. Later she and I wandered off on one of the many trails that crisscrossed Camp Leakey. I noticed she had a fresh scar on her arm, probably caused by one of the other adult females at Camp. Both of us sat down on the trail and I pulled out a tube of antibiotic cream from my shirt pocket. She immediately signed "food" to the tube of ointment. I signed "hurt" to her and pointed to the scar. I then opened the tube and dabbed some of the cream on the scar. She smelled it and signed "more" in poor form. So I applied a bit more to the scar. While I was doing that, I felt something going on behind me. To my surprise, Princess had put her right foot behind my back and was unzipping one of the pockets on the backpack I was wearing. While I was showing concern and attention to Princess's injury, she was deceptive in her attention toward me. Backpacks are known repositories of food and drink for the humans who wander the trails of Camp Leakey. So, while keeping my attention to her arm, she was pickpocketing me in search of an easy treat. Indeed, I would bring fruit bars and candy for her to practice her signs when I visited. I did pull out some fruit candy for her, asked her, "apa ini?" and she did correctly sign for it, "sweet food."

I left Camp Leakey shortly after that brief encounter but would return a few more times during that decade. The last time I saw Princess was in late 2011 with a group of family and friends taking an ecotour near the feeding station off the main trail. It was a wonderful encounter full of signing and rich interaction. Princess would love to join the humans in walking bipedally down the trails at Camp Leakey. She would hold onto the shoulder of one or two tourists, something we do not usually encourage, to help keep her upright while walking toward Camp. Princess was clearly a bi-cultural orangutan, comfortable in both Camp Leakey with humans and in the forest with the wildlife there. However, her status among adult orangutan females of Camp Leakey was not always favorable. Her injuries were caused by orangutans like Siswi, Siswoyo's first surviving offspring. Siswi inherited Siswoyo's alpha dominance position after Siswoyo died, and probably did not forget the times Princess would try to bite Siswi's mother years earlier. Siswi, Unyuk, and other more aggressive female orangutans would pick on Princess.

By the time I saw Princess in 2011, she was already underweight with her immune system compromised by parasites.

In 2012, Princess had lost so much weight due to the stress from the more dominant females, and possible parasitic infection, Galdikas took her to the Orangutan Care Center and Quarantine (OCCQ) in Pasir Panjang for medical care and rest to improve her health. At least that is the story I was told by Galdikas.

After several years at the Care Center, it was time for Princess to return to the forest. But management decided not to release her back to Camp Leakey where she would be attacked again. Instead, Princess and her daughter, Putri, were released in 2016 at an orangutan release area on another river system. A number of other ex-captive orangutans had been released there previously. For months, Princess and Putri would come to the feeding station almost daily for provisioning when food was not abundant in the local forest. Then one day Putri returned to the feeding station without her mother. Those that saw Putri said she appeared agitated.

Princess has not been seen since that day, and some feared that she might have died. Her disappearance seems to have been correlated to the appearance of an aggressive adult male orangutan who was known for forcing himself sexually on the female orangutans in the area. Like Schrödinger's Cat, Princess (aka my daughter) exists in a quantum state of being either alive or dead, and without evidence, my suspicion is that Princess, knowing the risks of surviving another pregnancy at her age, then in her mid-forties, left the area and has been living on her own, away from the aggressive male, within the vast peat swamp forest between where she was released and Camp Leakey. At least that is the story I choose to believe regarding this very smart and capable individual.

Other "Personalities of the Forest"

Is personality a uniquely human trait? I've demonstrated that that isn't the case, but anyone who keeps pets will say the same. Anyone with two dogs, for example, can easily see there are differences in their behavioral traits and temperament which collectively define each animal's unique personalities. Some dogs are friendlier than others. Some show qualities of bravery, while others are less inclined to bark or chase a stranger. The same is true with orangutans. Spend enough time with orangutans and their personality traits will be expressed. Princess as a youngster appeared to be lackadaisical during some of her signing lessons when compared to other orangutans of a similar age-class who appeared exuberant to learn signs. This may have been due to her enriched home-rearing with me which was mostly unstructured. Having to endure a formal sign training session was probably boring for Princess while it was exciting for other orangutans to get out of their safety enclosures to interact in the formal training session. While some may disagree, I believe that it is justifiable to anthropomorphize orangutans, specifically by attributing individual personality traits that are similar to those that we might recognize in a human child.

Behavioral traits that help to define one's personality are derived from inherited tendencies as well as learned behaviors. Captive and ex-captive rehabilitant orangutans, in general, are curious while wild orangutans are "decidedly uncurious" (Damerius , et al., 2017) and cautious when interacting with novel items.

Every orangutan I have ever gotten to know has unabashedly demonstrated their unique personalities in ways that are as recognizable as their fingerprints or face. I described my interactions with Rinnie and Princess earlier including aspects of their personality. Here are some of the other orangutan personalities I was privileged to have known.

Sugito and Gundul

Sugito and Gundul were two male orangutans whom I met early on at Camp Leakey. Sugito was the orangutan I was asked to teach signs to. He was suspected of drowning the younger orangutan named Doe. I was supposed to teach him enough to have him sign how or why he drowned Doe. While I wasn't able to interact with him in a manner to teach him signs, I was able to keep my eye on him. He didn't like interacting with people, with the exception of Galdikas, his adopted mother. Sugito liked watching the flow of people and orangutans from a high canopy vantage point. And he was a force to be reckoned with at Camp Leakey. He was smart and would mastermind the break-in of some of the buildings at the camp.

Sugito despised Galdikas's husband, Rod Brindamour, who was the camp co-director, and the feeling was mutual. Rod had to tolerate Sugito as a youngster when he was brought to Camp Leakey for rehabilitation. Galdikas decided the best way to begin the rehabilitation process was to adopt him and serve as his surrogate mother. That meant carrying him around all day while she conducted her research, taking him to bed to sleep, and bringing him to the dinner table for meals. As Galdikas attests in her book, *Reflections of Eden*, Brindamour and Sugito were not good buddies. And if Sugito urinated in bed, Brindamour had to deal with being that much more uncomfortable, as if the tropical heat wasn't bad enough.

When I arrived at Camp Leakey, Galdikas was in Los Angeles finishing up her doctorate and I had to deal with Sugito. Chasing him and others out of the dining hall with their hands full of our evening meal was not uncommon. Sugito would show his attitude towards me by unlacing my wet jungle boots on the porch and by dragging my clean, drying laundry that were draped over the bushy ferns through the dirt. Like Brindamour, we were not on good terms.

On one occasion when Galdikas was away, Sugito committed his grand act of larceny. On September 7, 1978, he and several other orangutans broke into the Galdikas's wooden home, which also served to secure chemical supplies for various needs, including preserving tissues, staining slides, medicines, and more. When I discovered the aftermath in the large multipurpose living room area, I literally cried: bottles of liquids and stains spilled all over the floor, glass everywhere, containers of food and other supplies scattered to the across the corners of the room. It took hours to clean up the mess.

When Rod Brindamour learned about Sugito's raid of his home upon his return to Camp Leakey on the night of September 9, he vowed to take action as we sipped drinks in the main room his camp house. Sugito broke the cardinal rule for a bi-cultural orangutan at Camp Leakey: as long as you were a sober citizen, you could stay. Once you became dangerous or a major nuisance, you lost that right. Sugito's raid caused the destruction of many of the items Rod valued. Knowing Rod was back in Camp, Sugito committed his final break-in and act of larceny September 11th, when he broke into the student housing and stole paperwork (data) and money. Rod decided it was time to relocate Sugito to another part of Tanjung Puting. Galdikas was away so she couldn't protest this severe action. And it was something for which she never forgave Rod – the banishment of her first "child".

So, the plan was put into action on September 22, 1978, when Sugito was captured by the Dayak staff and injected with Ketamine to put him into a deep sleep. We did not have transmitters or injectable microchips being used to track and identify wildlife at that time, so to recognize Sugito in the future, we decided to make an earring out of red nylon cord. We punctured his right ear, put the loop of cord through it, then heat-fused the ends into a solid ring.

We carried Sugito to the river and into the longboat. We traveled downstream to where the right branch forked into the Sekonyer River. Then we turned upstream and traveled to Natai Lengkuas, another area where a guard post had been built and where we could travel overland to a remote location in the forest. After carrying Sugito about thirty minutes into the nearby forest, we located a clearing and placed him on the ground. We all left the area, but because of the potential of bush pigs killing him, we waited until we saw him shake off the effects of the anesthetic. When we knew he was able to climb into a nearby tree we quickly and quietly left. That was the last we saw of Sugito, though some local people weeks later reported seeing an orangutan that matched his description along the river.

Then there's the case of Gundul, whose name means bald in the Indonesian language. And Gundul, like many male orangutans, had sparse hair on his head. I could relate as it was clear I was going bald in my mid-twenties. It ran in the family.

Anyway, when I first met Gundul, he kept his distance from me. Gundul's reputation preceded him, for he was the ornery subadult male orangutan who "raped" the camp cook. Galdikas gave the incident ample coverage in her book, *Reflections of Eden*. She was there when the deed took place across the river from Camp Leakey. Despite Galdikas's protestations and striking at Gundul, the amorous ape was relentless in his holding down the cook with his four effective hands and feet, and using his weight and strength to spread her legs while he attempted to penetrate her. Gundul eventually tired of this activity, perhaps because of the protestations of the two women, perhaps because he was satisfied. Both Galdikas and the cook were traumatized over the ordeal, and Galdikas told the cook they would keep the incident a secret. The cook, however, apparently found the incident too much to keep to herself, as it became the talk of camp shortly afterward.

Regardless, I had my own interactions with Gundul on several occasions. I described one of them earlier when I was with Rinnie. What was most interesting was the way in which Gundul feared me. Like with Rod Brindamour, Gundul feared my presence too, and while he was a terror around many of the Indonesians (particularly females), he would squeak like an infant if I got close to him. It may have been our slightly larger size, bearded face, or Western swagger that intimidated Gundul. On several occasions, I found I could simply get him to jump on my back to take him to a holding cage and relocate him across the river from Camp Leakey. He would, of course, find a way to get back to the camp side by crossing a fallen tree upriver especially when the water levels were low, but he never fought with me, not over a single thing. An interesting person.

Pola, Hampas, and Rantai

I would be remiss not to mention three of the four orangutans who served as drafted students for my doctoral research project. I have already discussed Princess at great length, but I also got to interact with Pola, Hampas, and Rantai on a regular basis, which allowed me to learn about their unique personalities as well. As drafted students, they did not seem happy tolerating the nearly 1-hour sign learning sessions that I subjected them to, except maybe Rantai. Rantai was a gangly, juvenile male who was highly active, loved to be tickled, and was eager to come to the classroom. Rantai means "chain" in Indonesian, and it was given to him by rescuers who freed him from chains. He loved to play and I remember having to exert a lot of energy to keep him sitting across from me. His level of attention was high, but like all the orangutans, Rantai was easily distracted from the sign-learning session. Nevertheless, he earned the nickname "The Professor", because he was the most studious during the training sessions and acquired the most signs of the four individuals.

Like Rantai, Hampas enjoyed getting out of the safety enclosure, but she was fussy and somewhat clumsy in the classroom, making sign training more challenging. She would knock over the sign referents and make squeaking sounds of frustration when she didn't get the rewards she anticipated. Hampas did not like to be tickled for enjoyment between trials, unlike Rantai.

Pola was the most difficult to work with during our sessions due to his aversion to the classroom. He often cried, tried to escape, and occasionally vanished into the forest, making him unavailable for training. As part of the home-reared group, Pola couldn't wait for the sessions to end and would quickly complete trials before leaving. Despite this, he became a dominant cheek padder at Camp Leakey many years later.

I vividly remember treating Pola for botflies when he was a juvenile. We lacked veterinarians and had to handle medical procedures ourselves. I had to anesthetize him and remove almost a dozen maggots from a wound on his face using kerosene to facilitate their extraction. Except for major surgeries, we had to take care of the primates' medical needs independently, as with Rantai, who once needed a subcutaneous tumor removed by a human doctor in town.

Siswoyo and Siswi

One of the first orangutans I met face-to-face at Camp Leakey was Siswoyo. She was a pregnant adult orangutan who had been living on the camp side of the river. Galdikas and Brindamour told me her story. She had been returned from captivity along with other orangutans from the private collection of a former general and chief of police for Indonesia and named after the wife of a forestry official. Siswoyo had been kept in a small cage for nearly six years and was semi-paralyzed from the waist down when she arrived at Camp Leakey. After her release and over time she gained back her physical strength and ability to walk. During one of her visits into the forest in early 1978, the dominant male of the area must have mated with her as she looked pregnant when Galdikas and Brindamour left Kalimantan for Southern California.

Before I arrived at Camp Leakey, Brindamour was intending to return before Siswoyo gave birth. His assignment by Galdikas was to film Siswoyo giving birth. However, for personal reasons, he spent extra time in Jakarta and did not return until the evening of September 9. It just so happened that in the early morning hours of September 9, Siswoyo gave birth in a tree a few meters away from the 200-meter boardwalk leading to camp. Thus, no film of the birth was shot, but I was able to photograph, too poorly unfortunately, Siswoyo and her newborn infant female with umbilical still attached whom

I named Siswi. Siswi was the first and only orangutan I named during my time at Camp Leakey. I held Siswi's afterbirth and placed it into the camp freezer, thinking it might have value to Galdikas upon her return. It didn't. Over the days and weeks to follow, I was able to observe this caring mother and her new infant as Siswi grew more alert and curious.

But Siswoyo was an orangutan for whom I had great affection. Not only was she the first orangutan at Camp Leakey to have given birth to a new generation of orangutans that did not carry the trauma of prior captivity, but she was also a kind soul and a great teacher. She was also the dominant adult female orangutan at Camp Leakey. On several occasions in the late afternoon, Siswoyo, carrying little Siswi, would approach a group of us sitting on the porch of the staff quarters and sit next to one of us. With her belly full of rice and forest vegetation, she would just sit and regurgitate the food she had eaten suggesting this was a way to extract more nutrients from the various foods she must have also eaten from the forest. After regurgitating onto the porch, she would slurp up the slurry and repeat the process. She was content and expressed her feelings towards me by taking my hand gently and just holding it while she continued to regurgitate her food.

During my stay at Camp Leakey, I witnessed a wide range of emotions displayed by Siswoyo from the sneering face of displeasure she made when she was scolded by the staff for stealing rice from the kitchen area to her slapping the ground in sheer delight when she saw me from a distance and then approached me to initiate a game of rough play. While I would not do such things today, we did have a friendship that called for occasional contact. Siswoyo allowed me to mold her hands needed to teach the sign for "food' as seen in National Geographic (Galdikas, 1980), something I am sad I was not able to not continue to do with her as I eventually had more orangutan students in formal programs.

I first started teaching Siswoyo signs on August 30, 1978, after a late morning visit to Rinnie and a raid of the kitchen by Sugito. Siswoyo and Rio, another large adolescent ape, came by my residence prompting me to go outside and try teaching them sign language. Using cookies as exemplars for food, I molded Siswoyo's hands two times and then she stole the bag of cookies from me. Later she regurgitated them to show Rio who successfully stole some of the liquified cookies. I wrote in my diary, "I get the impression that orangutans like showing off their stomach contents when leisurely relaxing."

Siswoyo and a young male orangutan named Toro ambled onto the porch of my residence the next morning. Siswoyo was spending time with Toro perhaps feeling the surging hormones of impending motherhood. I went outside to do some further training of signs with her over three different periods during the morning totaling over an hour. The longest period was 47 minutes.

But on a rainy September 3, 1978, the last day of Ramadan and only six days before Siswi was born, Siswoyo visited me on two occasions during which time I trained a few signs to her. As I wrote in my diary, "She basically likes sitting by me with her arm on mine. Even gave me a surprise kiss once. She still is grabby for food but the molding of "food" is getting easier."

Two days later Siswoyo paid me another morning visit on the guest house porch by herself. I took the opportunity to mold her hands for "leaf" and "flower" as I didn't have any food for her. Siswoyo's availability and generally kind nature made it tempting for me to practice teaching signs to an adult orangutan.

Even though she was an adult, I remember her wanting me to carry her on my back. Her favorite activity was getting into the hand wagon, a simple wooden, wheeled cart for transporting cargo from the boat to camp along the boardwalk. It was used to transport sacks of rice, sugar, and fruit and Siswoyo wasn't abashed about jumping in for a free ride. Because she was so well-natured, most of the staff had no problem letting her sit on a sack of rice for the trip along the boardwalk.

Over the years, many visitors and staff got to know Siswoyo and had their own special experiences. While I shared many close moments with Siswoyo during my initial two years at Camp Leakey, I will never forget the time she snuck aboard the camp kelotok and with the back of her hand, painted the interior of the vessel and herself green with the paint she found on the boat. With Siswi on her back, I discovered Siswoyo in the wheelhouse with an open can of green enamel paint smeared on various surfaces and all over her face. She sneered at me as I shooed her off the boat before she completed her masterpiece.

Siswi, Siswoyo's first offspring, was the first orangutan born to an ex-captive in Camp Leakey. Among all the ex-captives, Siswi's history was the most complete, as she was monitored throughout her life, from the day of her birth on September 9, 1978, until her death. As an adult, she enjoyed the status of being the dominant female ex-captive orangutan at Camp Leakey, having taken the mantle of dominance from her mother after she passed away in 1991. Siswi had her personal challenges over the years though. In the mid-1990's, Siswi suffered from a perforated intestine. A surgical veterinarian was flown in from Singapore and removed a small length of her intestine. While her prognosis was not good following surgery, Siswi recovered due to her strong will to live and the intense care given by the Camp staff. A few years later, the Orangutan Care Center and Quarantine facility in the town of Pasir Panjang were constructed and Siswi and other injured, unhealthy, or diseased orangutans were relocated there for a higher level of medical care than what could be offered at Camp Leakey.

Siswi grew up to become a flirtatious female among the adult male orangutans at Camp. She had a particularly close relationship with then-dominant Kusasi. When she felt in the mood, she would frequently approach him while he would be relaxing on the trails around Camp or in front of one of the structures. She would get on her back and reach toward Kusasi to grab his arm with her foot, teasing him, seeking his response.

I must admit I had conflicting feelings for Siswi. On the one hand, I had a wonderful relationship with her. When I was first at Camp Leakey, Siswi was a youngster and Siswoyo would let me interact with her. Over the years, Siswi would let me wrestle with her, just as I wrestled with her mom. But once her mother died, Siswi became a nemesis to Princess, my orangutan daughter. Siswi would bite Princess severely. So did Unyuk, another orangutan closer to Princess's age. Princess, it seemed, became low in the pecking order at Camp Leakey and Siswi was the alpha female among the females. In late 2021, Siswi passed away at 43 years of age according to an in-memoriam story on OFI's website. Princess hasn't been seen in many years.

Gallery Two

1. Rinnie, a free-ranging, ex-captive adult female orangutan who lived across the river from Camp Leakey.

2. Rinnie descending from a nearby tree to start her signing lesson.

3. Unlike other sign learning studies with great apes, Rinnie was free to participate by coming to the jungle classroom when her name was called. Here she wades through the swamp to join me.

4. Rinnie, deciding to come down from the trees to attend a signing session at the riverside class.

5. Rinnie signing for "nut" or "drink" as I reveal the exemplar.

6. With Princess in the prau watching, Rinnie approaches for her lessons at our riverside classroom.

7. During a riverside class, I mold Rinnie's hand for the sign "fruit" while showing her a piece of fruit.

8. At the riverside classroom, Rinnie attempts to make a sign.

9. Rinnie getting special attention as I tickle her between signing trials while other orangutans watch intentively.

10. With eyes watching, Rinnie receives her signing lesson at the feeding station.

11. One technique of training was to get Rinnie's attention and demonstrate the movement of the sign.

12. Rinnie practicing making the sign for "sweet" with candy as the exemplar for the sign.

13. Rinnie wiping herself after getting wet with a squirt bottle.

14. Using a squirt bottle to deliver water to Rinnie.

15. Rinnie relaxing on the feeding platform between sign-learning lessons. The intensity in her gaze and her occasional behavior revealed a remarkable grasp of "theory of mind."

16. While I hold up a peanut, Rinnie is making the sign for "nut".

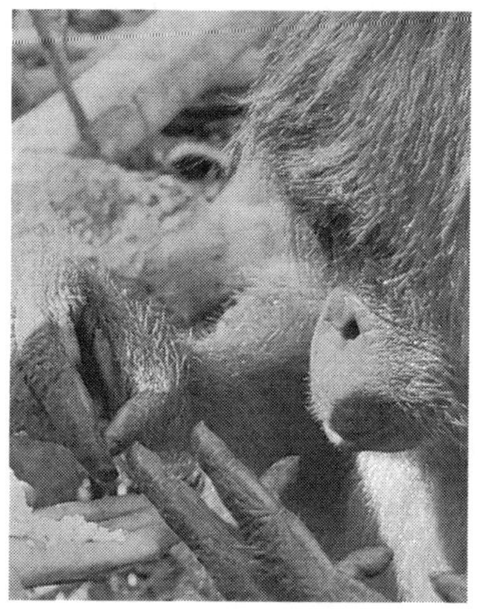

17. As she pulls on her extended finger, Rinnie signs for "rice" during a signing lesson.

18. Rinnie signing "biscuit" or cracker being held up by a Camp Leakey visitor during a signing lesson on the feeding platform across the river from Camp Leakey.

19. Princess, a juvenile female Bornean orangutan and my adopted daughter.

20. Young Princess joins me in a prau for a ride across the river.

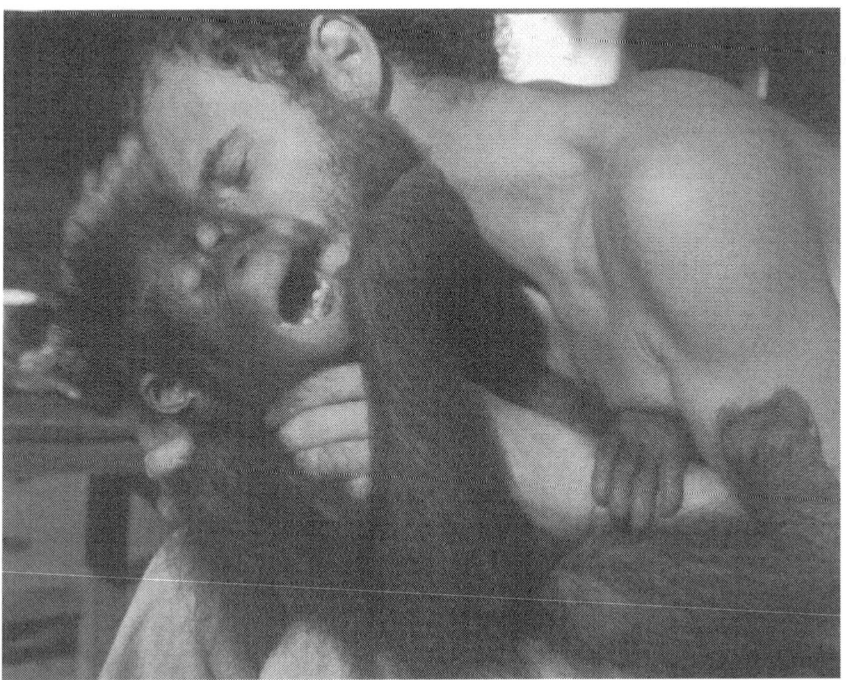

21. Between sign training lessons at our Camp Leakey residence, I give Princess a play bite and tickle her, an activity she loved and would sign "more" to repeat.

22. I show Princess a flower before molding the sign during a walk around Camp Leakey.

23. Princess felt reassured riding on my shoulder when I moved around Camp Leakey.

24. Princess holds onto me during a period of her life when she would have been clinging on to her own biological mother.

25. Princess resting with me between a sign learning lesson.

26. Princess riding on my shoulder directing me with the movement of her arms.

27. During a breakfast sign learning session, I guard the cup until she makes the sign for "drink".

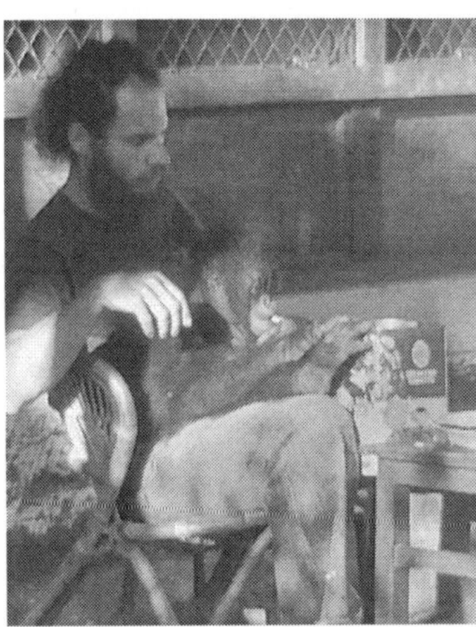

28. Princess taps the can of cookies before signing "open".

29. Princess enjoying the comfort of being inside of a woven bag.

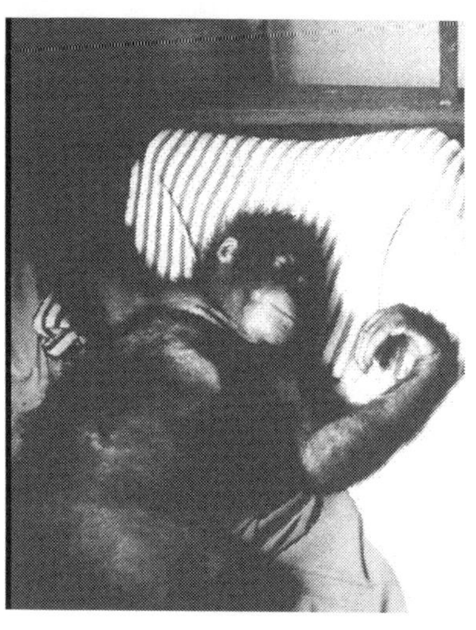

30. Princess sleeping in my bed.

31. Princess enjoying a piece of sugar cane on the porch of our jungle residence.

32. Princess practicing her climbing skills on a fruit tree at Camp Leakey.

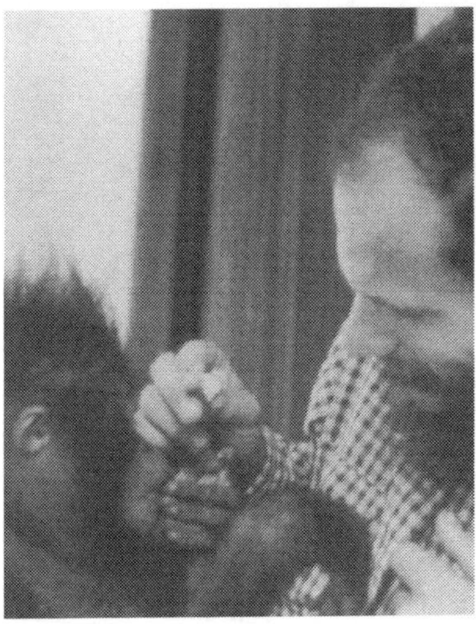

33. Princess makes a two-handed sign "you feed" with her right and left hand, respectively.

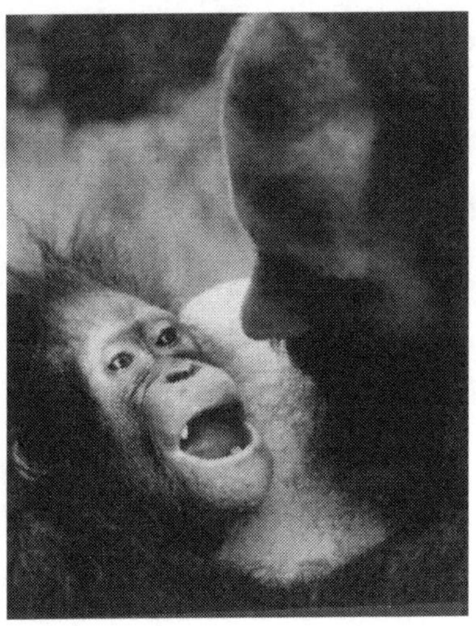

34. Princess would enjoy my blowing air into her mouth.

35. Student Toto manages Pola, one of my home-reared students while I take care of Princess during an afternoon sign learning session.

36. Conducting the special session lessons outside with a student from Jakarta.

37. With Princess clinging to my back, I bring Pola to the classroom for his lesson.

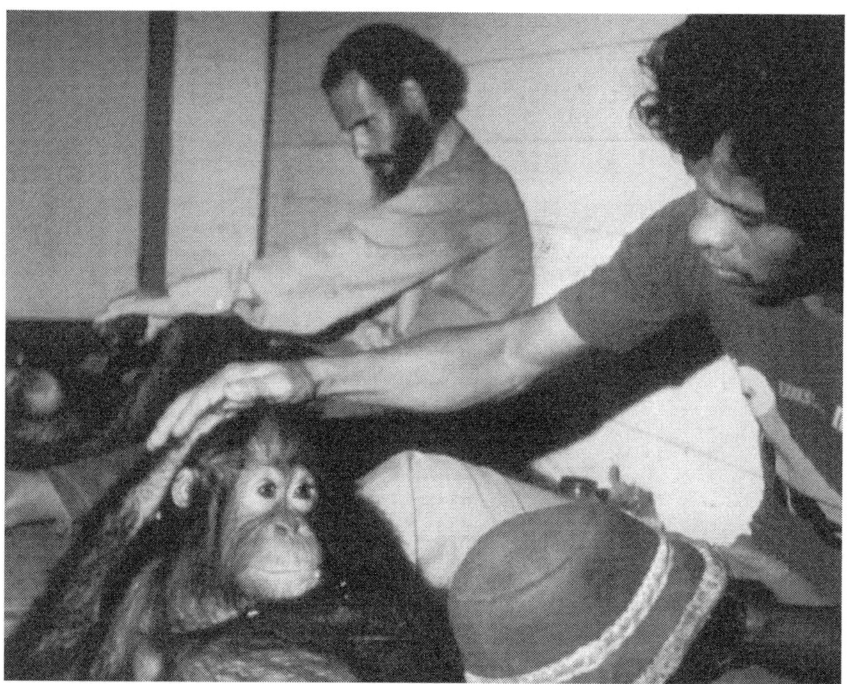

38. At the PPA house, Mudji, a student from Jakarta, molds Hampas's hand to form the sign for "hat" while showing her the hat referent as part of the Special Session.

39. My attempt to imitate an arboreal ape with Siswoyo and daughter Siswi.

40. Siswoyo with daughter Siswi after painting the kelotok green.

41. Siswoyo carrying Siswi in the peat swamp forest.

42. My fiancée Inggriani and I visit with Princess and her first offspring Prince in 1986.

43. Molding Princess's hand during one of my visits to Camp Leakey in the late 1980s.

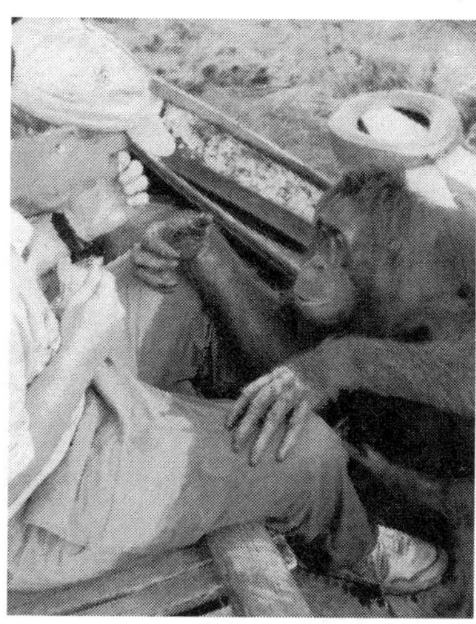

44. Princess interested in some treats during a visit to Camp Leakey in the 2000s.

45. During my last meeting with Princess, she signs "more" to me to obtain another treat.

46. I sign to Princess during a private ecotour to Camp Leakey in November 2011.

47. The last photograph I took of Princess and her offspring, Putri, in November 2011, as she walked off into the forest.

48. Large plantations at the turn of the 20th century: one of the gravest threats to orangutans.

49. A gold mining camp outside of Tanjung Puting National Park threatens ecological integrity.

50. In this flyover, two threats to the primary and secondary forests are visible: gold mining in the foreground and palm oil plantations in the background.

A Passion Forged

I have spent a half century dedicated to better understanding and saving orangutans and their habitat. While holding down full-time government jobs for over thirty years, I helped create and administer organizations whose missions have been nothing short of ensuring the long-term survival of the species and their rainforest habitat. Saving such species also means saving individual orangutans. Tilting at windmills in a Quixotic fantasy? I think not. But if so, I am not alone. There are thousands of people around the globe devoted to helping other threatened species and ecosystems. Such noble pursuits to "save the world" and its animal inhabitants are not without pain and personal sacrifices. Like Jane Goodall (and Dian Fossey and Biruté Galdikas), somewhere in my journey, I realized that the health and continuation of the orangutans and their homes is also a human moral and ecological concern. Jane Goodall's story impacted me and my passion for orangutans, but at the time when I first met her, I didn't know that.

I came to know Jane Goodall by chance in 1970 or 1971 when I was a marine biology/pre-med major at Sierra College, a small community college located in Rocklin, California, just east of Sacramento. Because I was dating the college vice-president's daughter at the time, I frequented the college's administration building. One day, I was in the building and was asked by someone in the administrative office (perhaps the vice-president himself?) if I was interested in picking up Jane Goodall at the airport. The college had booked her for an evening presentation about chimpanzees. I had read about her groundbreaking work in National Geographic magazine regarding her research in Gombe Stream National Park, but frankly, I would have been more interested in meeting the marine biologist Jacques Cousteau, a childhood hero. Nevertheless, I happily agreed. So, with a campus car, I picked her up at the airport in Sacramento and brought her to her hotel to freshen up before taking her to her evening lecture. I remember sitting pensively on the edge of her bed as she made a phone call to invite R. Allen and Beatrix Gardner to attend her presentation. This husband and wife team had taught the chimpanzee Washoe sign language just a few years earlier (Gardner & Gardner, 1969). Jane seemed fascinated with the work of the Gardners. She clearly saw aspects of rich gesturing with her own study population. The Gardners accepted the invitation and drove two hours across the Sierra Nevadas on Highway 80 from Reno to the Rocklin, California campus.

That night I sat next to the Gardners in the front row of the college's largest auditorium and made small talk before Goodall spoke eloquently about the complex interpersonal relationships of the Gombe chimpanzees and other human-like behaviors they demonstrated. As fate would have it, both Goodall and the Gardners would become my academic aunt and grandparents, respectively, in the years ahead, and I would enter Tanjung Puting at the same age Jane entered Gombe.

Two years later, I circuitously ended up at Fresno State College where I graduated with a bachelor's degree in zoology and was pursuing a master's in biology. There, my animal behavior professor, Richard Haas, connected me with zoo director Paul Chaffee at the Fresno City Zoo, thus sparking my interest in orangutans. I decided on a master's thesis: teaching sign language to a juvenile orangutan. No one had ever tried this. However, as mentioned in my first chapter, I eventually used the methods of David Premack (1971). Interestingly, it was the Gardners who suggested I employ Premack's artificial symbol technique to allow for faster results.

When I graduated in 1975 and did not get accepted into my desired program, I contacted Roger Fouts, the Gardners's star graduate student who had taken Washoe from Reno to the Institute for Primate Studies (IPS) near the University of Oklahoma. A book written about his work interested me (Linden, 1974). He was an assistant professor in the department of psychology at the time and invited me to pursue my Ph.D. within the department of zoology where I could work across campus with him as my major professor.

It was there, between taking classes and teaching as a graduate teaching assistant, that I found myself spending time at the IPS to interact with the chimpanzee population housed and administered by the bald and burly psychiatrist William Lemmon. A lot has been written about Lemmon (Hess, 2008), but I had few negative run-ins with him. I was content to meet and work with the chimpanzees that lived in the caged compound. Bruno, Booee, Thelma, Poncho, Washoe, and many others were among the adult chimpanzees that had different personalities and temperaments. All of them were confined and some, like Washoe and Poncho, were taken out for occasional walks in the most isolated part of Lemmon's Oklahoma property east of the university campus. The chimpanzees were generally kept on a leash and handlers would take a cattle prod with them. I learned that while they were easy to hold and handle as youngsters, the older adolescent and adult chimpanzees could be dangerous to be around. The chimp compound was like a prison with large males displaying, vocalizing raucously, pounding metal doors, and making loud noises frightening to the uninitiated. It was clear they were unhappy being locked in their enclosures, made even more mad by some being let out to walk. Fast, strong, and with strong hands and sharp teeth, an angry and jealous chimpanzee was no match to any human who was the target of his aggression. Yet William Lemmon could lead most of the chimpanzees that managed to escape back into their enclosures merely by taking them by their hand and walking them back. He had to be the alpha male.

Even with the nearly adolescent chimpanzees like Ally, brother of the famous Nim Chimpsky (Hess, 2008; Inggersol & Scarnà, 2023), the danger was always brewing. As Fouts would tell me, "They are always testing you, looking for your weak spots." Fouts knew it took a special person to be able to work with chimpanzees, and he wasn't sure about me. Chimpanzee youngsters love to play. In chimpanzee societies, play blends into rough play, which merges into tests of dominance, a slap here, and a shoulder check there. Eventually play fighting escalates into real aggressive behavior with biting, scratching, and kicking. One of the two contestants becomes the winner, and the winner of most bouts will usually become dominant in the future, leading to less aggressive interactions when the two encounter each other.

Indeed, chimpanzees try to exert their dominance over the humans that come into their lives. A new student is tested in the same way as a chimp: it starts with play fighting and if that student doesn't quickly assert dominance, the chimpanzee will eventually dominate the student, and blood will be drawn, a chimpian victor. When I m, et ally, already a talented signing chimpanzee, I decided he would be my student. He was raised in a Catholic home while learning sign language as a youngster. It was thought that Ally had developed the concept of God as he would point upwards to the heavens when asked about the location of the Almighty. He also knew the sign of the cross. But despite his possible spiritual enlightenment, he was still a chimpanzee. In the first few meetings I had with Ally, Fouts became concerned. "Gary, you have 'bite me' written all over you," Fouts would say, more than once. Ally's play was getting increasingly physical with me after all. Fouts insisted I had to have a one-on-one encounter with Ally that was swift and firm to allow me to be dominant over him. And so, one day, I did. He never challenged me after that.

While working with Ally and preparing him to be part of a study examining comprehension of signs by a chimpanzee, I received the fateful call from Fouts on July 5, 1977, the call that started me on my journey.

Living among a free-ranging population of ex-captive orangutans of various age-classes and getting to know individuals deepened my passion toward orangutans and appreciation of the plight they faced at the time. Indeed, while serving as co-director of Camp Leakey, I did witness the untimely deaths of several orangutans. Epong, for instance, was an ex-captive juvenile orangutan who was clumsy and may have suffered from a neurological or vision problem. He was living across the river with Rinnie and other free-ranging orangutans who were provisioned but able to explore the swamp forest across the river from Camp Leakey. One day Epong did not appear at the afternoon feeding, and days later his body was discovered. We surmise he fell from a tree and died. Darwinian selection is unforgiving and startlingly common in the natural world.

While death among the orangutan population is inevitable, it has an emotional impact on those who are deeply connected with certain individuals. I am particularly affected by the life and death of a juvenile orangutan named Jimmy. Jimmy's death was one, I believe, of a broken heart. It clearly showed me that orangutans are as sensitive to the loss of a mother figure as we all are.

The Story of Jimmy

Because it is illegal under Indonesian law to own orangutans as pets, people who are found keeping them as surrogate children or pets are required to turn them in or have them confiscated by the authorities – the conservation branch of the Forestry Department. A fine could be imposed, but generally, it is not. The Forestry Department, in turn, sends the orphaned orangutan to an institution for rehabilitation or reintroduction into the wild. In the case of the young male orangutan named Jimmy (approximately six years old), his elderly human mother, an Indonesian woman of Chinese descent, brought Jimmy to Camp Leakey in May 1979 to begin his process of rehabilitation. We would integrate him into the free-ranging population of ex-captives who would learn skills from each other while being monitored by the Dayak staff. It was an informal training method employed at Camp Leakey at the time. I remember the somber face on the woman as she spent several days at Camp Leakey making sure her adopted son would be in good hands. Jimmy had bonded very closely to the woman, a mother figure who replaced his natural mother killed years earlier thereby bringing Jimmy into the illegal pet trade. We don't know how the woman came to acquire Jimmy, but it was clear both she and Jimmy loved each other and dreaded the separation that was inevitable later that day. Some of us at Camp Leakey tried to get Jimmy to play with the younger orangutans in the area, but he was not interested in the least. He retreated to the arms of a caregiver, someone other than his adopted mother as we wanted to distract him from her whereabouts. Eventually, the woman slowly and tearfully made her way down the two-hundred-meter boardwalk to the jetty where she departed from Camp Leakey by boat.

Jimmy stopped eating on his own after that day. He was obviously depressed and we found ourselves having to encourage him to eat fruits and rice, just so he could get the energy needed to sustain himself. But Jimmy didn't want to eat, and he lost weight. Was it parasites? Having previously used the microscope at Galdikas's house to look for eggs of parasitic roundworms, I checked his stool and he was clean. It seemed as if his adopted mother was the only one he trusted for food. We worked hard to get Jimmy to take interest in the activities around Camp Leakey; he slowly started to accept his new situation. To help him gain vitality, we would give him vitamin shots. By late June 1979, Jimmy was improving with his appetite and weight. Just as Jimmy seemed to be on the road to becoming rehabilitated with the other orangutans, the worst possible thing happened.

On July 9, 1979, Jimmy's adopted mother and her grandchildren visited Camp Leakey to see her former surrogate ape-child. Jimmy was very excited to see the older woman. He climbed into her arms and hugged her as he had two months earlier before the separation. She smiled with tears in her eyes as she reciprocated the hugging during the brief moments at Camp. Eventually, the woman and her grandchildren left Camp Leakey, and Jimmy slid back into a state of depression.

Over the next month, Jimmy refused to eat and by my twenty-eighth birthday a month later, I was giving medications to Jimmy. It was clear to me, and others, that Jimmy missed his adopted mother to such a degree it was impacting his health. I remembered thinking about how enforcing the law regarding orangutan ownership sometimes seemed unfair to the individuals, certainly to Jimmy and his adopted mother. I had never before seen such a close bond and the devastating effect of breaking it because of a legally compelled separation.

During the rest of August 1979, Jimmy continued to waste away. We tried force-feeding him with a tube when he refused to eat even the most basic foods. I will never forget the day when Jimmy died in my arms on September 2, 1979. He simply lost the will to live. I cried that day. I finally understood what it meant to truly lose all hope.

The reintroduction process presently followed at the various care centers on Borneo and Sumatra thankfully do not allow another case like Jimmy's to occur. The protocols today are much more stringent than in the early days at Camp Leakey. Contact from the general public is generally forbidden for physical and psychological reasons. While all orphaned orangutans suffer psychologically from the killing of the primary mother (frequently in front of the baby), most ex-captives that come from a human home do not suffer as much as Jimmy did following the separation from the secondary mother. Most do not refuse food and eventually find another youngster to hold onto during periods of stress and insecurity. But it was this tragedy that pointed out the similarities in emotions, the primal need for maternal love, the heartbreaking outcome of that love lost, that deepened my connection to orangutans.

Each cute orangutan that you see at a rescue and care center has his or her own story of horror. Every individual witnessed his or her mother killed in a brutal way forcing the baby to become an orphan during the most intimate and formative period in the young ape's life. This is the time when the infant would be clinging to the mother, nursing on demand, and observing the feeding patterns of the mother to learn what is safe to eat in the future. The mother would spend many moments during the day caring for the bodily needs of the infant, cleaning, and grooming with lips and fingers, showing a level of affection that rivals the love of a human mother and child.

When an infant orangutan is pulled away from the dying or dead body of her mother by poachers, she mightily clings and cries. The sound can be hair-raising and shocking coming from a body so small. The frightened infant is surprised and horrified her mother is not coming to the rescue, not yet understanding death. The mother would normally reach out or climb to the location of the terrified youngster after she practices climbing or locomoting. Whimpering sounds, when feeling insecure, would ensure a return by the mother. This practice and retrieval are repeated by the infant and mother over many months as the youngster learns how to maneuver in the canopy of the rainforest. Eventually, the mother stops retrieving the youngster once she sees how skilled her offspring becomes, even when the crying starts. The young orangutan orphan is thus fast tracked to growing up without the long and loving tutelage of the biological mother.

It is understandable, then, that these orphan orangutans show signs of abnormal behavior when in the care centers. If they were human, we would call it PTSD. Some refuse to be held, choosing to hug themselves and rock back and forth. If one can hug another youngster to obtain comfort, it becomes a stop-gap measure on a long road to independence. Others, like Jimmy, may never live to return to the forests from where they were born, for various reasons including the individual's inability to locomote and find food in the forest (due to loss of limbs or being blind from pellet gun attacks), individuals having an actively transmissible disease (e.g., hepatitis) that could spread to others in the population, behavioral problems that could threaten other orangutans adversely, and increasingly, fewer protected forests for their release, especially in the regions where they were born.

For all the thousands of ex-captive orangutans who have been rescued from the illegal pet trade and brought to rehabilitation and reintroduction centers, six to eight times as many have died as infants brought to the black market. While in the field, the risk of being killed during the capture is high, the mortality during handling and transport is even higher. Besides the psychological trauma of witnessing the death and separation from the mother, the stress of physical handling, being packed together with other youngsters to avoid detection, and the lack of water and appropriate nutrients means that only a fraction of the total number of orphaned orangutans captured arrives at the marketplace alive in Jakarta, Medan, or other cities. It is a staggering total and one that often causes statisticians and busy politicians to forget the horror faced by each individual orangutan baby. But let's talk for a moment about those numbers without considering the personal tragedies faced by each orangutan person.

I was shocked to learn in early 2018 from a multi-author study (Voigt, et al., 2018) that over one hundred thousand orangutans had been lost from the forests of Borneo during a sixteen-year period (1999-2015). These losses, a usefully numbing euphemism for deaths, were the result of the habitat destruction driven by the demand for timber, mining, and estate plantations, especially for pulp paper and palm oil. Without forest habitat, orangutans compete for limited food and many will die. But orangutans were also disappearing from within forested areas suggesting that direct killing was also happening. To make matters worse, some seventy-five percent of orangutans were found to be outside of protected national parks and nature reserves.

This news came as a surprise to me and many others who for years have been saying that while the situation was dire, there were fifty-four thousand orangutans remaining on Borneo (Wich, et. Al, 2008). We were wrong. Estimates over the years have changed, but this new revelation suggested that there were three to four times as many orangutans before the turn of the twenty-first century. Not surprisingly, the decimation and fragmentation of remaining forests in conjunction with orangutan populations prompted the International Union for the Conservation of Nature (IUCN) to reclassify the Bornean orangutan's conservation status in their well-known "Red Book" from Endangered to Critically Endangered in 2016. If action wasn't taken in the forested areas to combat the killing of orangutans, there was a high likelihood the smaller breeding population (metapopulations) would be driven to extinction in short order.

Even by when I had first arrived, environmental degradation within the protected Tanjung Puting reserve was already evident. Illegal logging was the main driver of deforestation at the time. Taking a walk within the Camp Leakey study area was and still is enough to illustrate this fact. Enormous, partially hewed hardwood tree trunks are scattered throughout the trail system, like petrified corpses of giants.

OFI

By mid-1979, the funds from the National Geographic Society and The Leakey Foundation were drying up, which meant we needed new grants to continue to research, help, and protect the orangutan people. On August 24, 1979, I met Galdikas in her Camp Leakey office to coordinate on Camp matters, and we discussed the dire fiscal situation we were in. We jointly decided to create a nonprofit organization to support our work at the Orangutan Research and Conservation Project at Camp Leakey. As a result, I left Tanjung Puting in 1980 with my data and a couple hundred dollars from Galdikas to start the process of establishing an organization, what we were calling Camp Leakey West.

One of the first people I approached on my return to Los Angeles was Norman Lear, legendary TV producer ("All in the Family" and "The Jeffersons"), who had donated two VHS tape decks to Galdikas so I could videotape my signing research at Camp Leakey. Interestingly, Galdikas apparently babysat Lear's daughters when she attended UCLA years earlier, hence her connection to him. When I met Lear in his Century City offices for a brief meeting, I wanted to express my appreciation for his prior generosity while we discussed Camp Leakey West, but keeping his attention was a challenge. Understandably so though, as he was busy shifting his time between me and a call with Ted Kennedy, who was then running against incumbent Jimmy Carter for the Democratic nomination for president. In the end, I did manage to properly thank him and asked him to join the foundation that we would eventually create, which to my delight, he agreed.

Getting such a prominent person on our board was the only remaining hurdle Galdikas and I had to develop our organization, so after sharing the news, we immediately reached out to a lawyer named John Beal, who had visited Camp Leakey in 1979. It literally took years to finally form our 501(c)(3) nonprofit, as there were no turn-key legal services at the time to facilitate the formation of a non-profit corporation. Despite the lengthy delay, the organization, now named The Orangutan Foundation, was finally incorporated in 1986 with Galdikas as president and me as vice president, Blanche Whittey as treasurer, and John Beal as secretary. Our board consisted of Norman Lear, Gerry Sugarman, and Bohap bin Jalan, Galdikas's new husband.

While the board celebrated our formal incorporation in Los Angeles, I was, perhaps fatefully, back at Camp Leakey, fully immersed in my self-funded research project. However, this time, my research was not focused on orangutans. Instead, it revolved around studying the blackwater river ecosystem. This research project came about after I had recently proposed to Inggriani, whom I had met on the day of my doctoral exam. Though the details of this arrangement affected me during my six-month long study on the river, it affected my future wife more as I eventually tuned out what was going on back home. My dedication to my work and the foundation almost led to our breakup, which is why I decided to end my research to prioritize mending my relationship with my fiancée. But, after finally stabilizing my relationship with Inggriani and marrying her, I once again turned all of my focus back to the Orangutan Foundation.

While I was still working full-time for the federal and state government, I devoted my Fridays, weekends, and many weeknights to volunteer at the Foundation's office. Interestingly, the office itself was located in one of Galdikas's parents' rental apartments in the Brentwood area of West Los Angeles. Galdikas had a clever arrangement with her mother, Filomena, where the Foundation paid a fair price for using the apartment as an office, and in return, Filomena supported us as a dedicated office manager.

In those early months, though I enjoyed Filomena's hospitality with rugelach and coffee, I faced the critical challenge of understanding the intricacies of running a nonprofit organization, like organizing the foundation's computer system and website, motivating board members, and navigating state and federal laws. I also had to learn many new skills, like graphic design, but I really enjoyed editing the foundation's newsletter. All of this was to raise awareness and make the case for public funding, a requirement of operating a nonprofit organization and something that was an ongoing struggle in those early days.

Lacking the financial resources to hire a professional executive director or grant writer, much less the ability to do it myself, we had no choice but to depend on volunteers, which I still was at the time.

One of our early and impactful initiatives, which effectively engaged our volunteers, was organizing mailing parties to secure widespread sponsorships and expand our mailing list. Inggriani would consent to hosting these events at our 700 square-foot apartment. With the promise of pizza and soda, we'd invite the local volunteers over to stuff and sort hundreds of envelopes. These campaigns were successful, which I could only attribute to my wife's support and my volunteers' passion to build our organization.

As our organization's funding grew with our mailing list, we established multiple chapters in different countries, including Indonesia, Taiwan, England, and Canada. I personally oversaw this expansion which was quite a remarkable journey. Throughout this process, I played various roles and took on multiple responsibilities to ensure the success of our organization. Eventually, we decided to change our official name to Orangutan Foundation International, or OFI, as we felt we needed a more fitting name to reflect our increasingly transnational efforts.

This growth came at a high cost, however, one that I didn't fully realize until later. Just like with my research project on the blackwater river ecosystem, my dedication to the project turned me into a simple and stubborn creature, consumed by my efforts to save the orangutans. This time, however, I lost sight of myself, completely unwilling to notice the toll it was taking on me and my relationships. This personal trauma was profound, not something I say lightly, but it allowed me to achieve significant accomplishments across multiple continents.

For example, in the late 1980s, I received word from Marcus Phipps, a Canadian teaching in Taiwan, of a burgeoning trade in orangutans on that island. Naturally, I took a trip to Taipei to investigate the situation and encouraged him to establish a chapter of OFI. The trip was an eye-opening visit that was as much as a culture shock to me as my first visit to Jakarta a decade earlier.

During my tours with Marcus, I saw many orangutan abuses and was horrified by the sight of an orangutan chained up in one of the establishments in the notorious "Snake Alley". It was abundantly clear that while Taiwan had become a signatory to the Convention on International Trade in Endangered Species of Wild Fauna and Flora (CITES) in 1985, Taiwan's agency for endangered species had not actually created or enforced any laws prohibiting the import of species banned by CITES.

After realizing the severity of what I was witnessing, Marcus and I organized a meeting with officials from the Taipei Zoo, which housed a significant number of orangutans abandoned by their owners due to their destructive behavior as exotic pets. Despite battling an intense headache caused by the horrors I had just seen, we successfully coordinated a local press event to communicate our intentions and highlight the severe consequences of engaging in internationally illegal trade.

After this, we immediately established the Orangutan Foundation Taiwan, with Marcus at its helm, to address the issue of orangutans forcibly residing on the foreign island. Through our efforts, we accomplished two significant actions: raising public awareness about the conservation implications of the illegal trade and organizing clinics to provide much-needed medical care to the smuggled orangutans.

While Taiwan's endangered species agency did eventually help pass a law closing the loophole on the sale of orangutans, the lure of an orangutan as a pet had already begun to fade by then, as their owners tired of the destruction and expenses their prized pets usually caused. Due to this sudden disinterest, most of the orangutans sold to Taiwan surely died in captivity from lack of proper care, though some others were simply set free to wander the streets of Taipei and many of the final survivors were sent to sanctuaries and zoos in Taiwan. A small number of confiscated orangutans were successfully repatriated to Indonesia through efforts of OFI (not under my direct oversight) and others, however, including the first celebrated group called the "Taiwan Ten" (IPPL, 1991).

The return of the "Taiwan Ten" to Indonesia was met with tremendous media attention. The initial plan was for them to be returned to Tanjung Puting, but they were quarantined and later maintained at the Jakarta Zoo with the help of students from the Universitas Nasional and OFI caregivers from Camp Leakey. I made sure funds were being sent to Indonesia to support this long vigil. This went on for 11 months while their fate was being determined by the Indonesian government, then the head of the Indonesia's nature and wildlife protection agency reneged on returning the orangutans to the forests of Tanjung Puting to send them elsewhere. This was extremely concerning, because I personally knew some of the students and all of them would oppose this decision putting them at odds with the national government. Indeed, a group of students from Universitas Nasional, some former students of Galdikas, became irate and began protesting this new change in plans. They vowed to not turn the "Taiwan Ten" over to the authorities.

Though the students' protests were not of the political variety more commonly seen in Indonesia, the Forestry Department did not take kindly to this. After Galdikas learned of a military style raid of the zoo being planned in early November 1991, she called me late at night to tell me of her sudden plans to seek safe harbor. She also relayed the government's plans to the students, which gave them the time to put their own plan together: on the night before the raid, nine of the ten orangutans were swaddled like human babies and taken from the zoo. The students used multiple taxis, changing them frequently to evade the authorities, driving all night long around the streets of Jakarta. The military raid at dawn yielded a single large and very irate orangutan and 100 protesting students and conservationists. Afterwards, the nine sequestered orangutans were presented to the office of the Minister of Environment as a trusted authority, but the fate of the "Taiwan Ten" didn't ultimately have the happy ending the students had hoped for: fourteen of the students were beaten and jailed, though later released by the police, and the healthiest orangutans were sent back to either a reintroduction center in East Kalimantan or to a primate research facility in Bogor, Java.

While other foreign countries, like Thailand (IPPL, 1990), were also hotspots for illegal orangutan trade, the domestic illegal trade in orangutans was even more relentless. Forests inside and outside Tanjung Puting National Park were cleared for timber and agriculture including palm oil. Male and female adult orangutans were killed in gardens, orchards, and plantations while babies and juveniles were sold to be caged or chained as pets in villages and frequently behind the homes of police and military officials. While Camp Leakey was closed to new releases of ex-captives, other parts of Tanjung Puting and surrounding areas were being established by OFI and the Parks Department as places to relocate ex-captives. The influx became so great in the 90s that developing an additional Orangutan Care Center and Quarantine (OCCQ) facility was necessary to prepare for the eventual rehabilitation and reintroduction of new arrivals.

This period proved to be a busy time for both OFI and me. In July 1991, my first human child, Jason, was born, yet I remained dedicated to expanding OFI domestically and internationally. This was a pressure point, and though my wife eloquently spoke about OFI's mission during our travels, she wasn't always happy with my focus on OFI over helping with our baby. Despite her brewing resentment, she kept it largely to herself during those years, which was helpful since Galdikas was able to convince the Indonesian government to hold the Second Great Apes of the World Conference in Jakarta and Tanjung Puting in December 1991. OFI would be the conference organizer, which meant I was given a larger responsibility of coordinating the event.

Organizing a Major Conference

The first Great Apes Conference was held seventeen years earlier in a secluded castle in Austria and featured two dozen field and captive ape researchers, including Jane Goodall, Dian Fossey, Roger Fouts, and Galdikas. It was that conference that brought Fouts's research to Galdikas's attention, hence my connection to Galdikas through Fouts. Now, thanks to Galdikas's selling the idea to a high government official, I was responsible for overseeing the development of the second Great Apes Conference, which required bringing Jane Goodall and dozens of other great ape researchers to Indonesia. Why Jane Goodall? Besides the obvious reasons, she was already known by government minister Susilo Sudarman, who had been smitten by her persona, and Galdikas was also selling the idea that Jane would attract the best talent and primate loving tourists to this last official event of "Visit Indonesia Year 1991." She dropped this project on my lap, and I was not at all ready for it.

It was hard enough trying to balance my personal life with the amount of work I was already doing at the OFI office. Now, the level of work was magnified and without funding support from the Indonesian government to hire a professional to produce the conference program and enroll the expert attendees, it was all left to me and a handful of volunteers. More long nights at the office following my day job with the State of California, desperately struggling to raise funds from U.S. corporate sponsors working in Indonesia to ensure we would have enough to fly our expert researchers to Jakarta.

I eventually worked with the Director General of Tourism, Joop Ave, to coordinate a series of events: a pre-conference ecotour to Sumatra, the major opening at the Presidential Palace, and the breakout sessions and workshops in Tanjung Puting. Because of his power and influence, Minister Sudarman had arranged to have a large parabolic satellite dish dropped behind the Rimba Lodge located on the Sekonyer River across from the national park. Sudarman wanted to make sure the participants would be able to call home from special wall phones mounted in the lodge. He also had special orangutan stamps made commemorating the conference and convinced the government to issue a new five-hundred rupiah note featuring an orangutan a year later.

Despite the whirlwind coordination, the conference was opened with a few hundred people assembled at the Presidential Palace. I sat up front with Galdikas and my wife, waiting patiently while my stomach was in knots. Finally, President Soeharto, a man who had decisively ruled Indonesia for a quarter century, walked slowly to the podium and gave the keynote address about the importance of great apes. Galdikas and I smiled, as we had helped the ministry with some of the President's talking points, including the importance of great apes, their being endangered, and the pride that Indonesia had for being caretaker of the orangutans. When he had finished, Jane Goodall, as we had planned, gave her signature performance of the chimpanzee pant hoot, and I followed with the orangutan long call. I felt so much honor and pride as I looked down on the shiny marble floor, closed my eyes, and invoked the spirit of countless male orangutans who have been announcing their presence and defending their home range across the millennia. I gave an abbreviated version of the call, from the low frequency beginning to the higher frequency middle, that sounds a bit like a lion's roar, then to the ending portion, which transitions back to a lower frequency for an after-burbling sound. I smiled as the crowd applauded my performance.

The plenary sessions at the palace featured the main speakers, Herman Rijksen, Jane Goodall, Galdikas and Kelly Stewart. Stewart, daughter of actor Jimmy Stewart, was the keynote speaker on gorillas. Besides being a researcher herself, Stewart was the perfect stand in for Dian Fossey, who was murdered years earlier in Africa. While each woman spoke eloquently about their respective great ape counterparts, Rijksen, a Dutchman, used the occasion to lament over the state of affairs of the orangutan, frequently making criticisms of the way the species was being managed by the host country. He projected a colonialist attitude (perhaps the Dutch could do better?), and I was immediately embarrassed for our generous hosts, the Indonesian government. Galdikas, on the other hand, was on her best behavior and avoided the Minister of Forestry, due to the controversy surrounding the Taiwan Ten. She wanted no issues, as she was only being protected by Emil Salim, the Minister of Environment, and Susilo Sudarman, the Minister of Tourism, Telecom, and Post, the very man who ensured this conference even happened.

I was relieved when the high pressure opening ended and I could focus on shepherding the selected attendees, mainly researchers and academics, to Borneo in chartered airplanes. Once in Pangkalan Bun, a brief welcoming ceremony was held followed by the group heading up the Sekonyer River to the Rimba Lodge, where numerous presentations and workshop sessions were held in a large meeting hall over several days. Only the active presenters were able to participate in this part of the conference, as lodging space was extremely limited, which was partly why high-ranking officials opted for day visits using speedboats and chose to stay at the more luxurious hotels back in Pangkalan Bun.

It was a colorful affair with the resident population of long-tailed macaques occasionally leaping from the trees or the roofs of the Rimba Lodge to harass the participating primatologists, most of whom enjoyed the interspecies interaction. Like the hyperactive monkeys, I found myself scurrying over the swampy ironwood walkways to help orchestrate the next sessions, which were focused on the presenter's most recent field research on their specific great apes. Most of those turned into presentations on great ape biology, behavior, ethics, psychology, or ecology and seemed unrelated to the official subtitle of the conference that resonated with President Soeharto's New Order administration at the time: "Conservation of the great apes in the new world order of the environment."

One of the tasks given to the assembled group of attendees was crafting the conference findings and preparing the main points for a formal proclamation. This challenge proved to be an argumentative exercise by many of the attendees, several of whom felt quite passionate about what was put in and what was kept out of the final drafts. I tried to stay engaged in the different workgroups but mainly helped to keep the momentum going, except on those rare moments when I could slip away from the dozens of participants to take a break. On one occasion during an evening work session, I found myself alone with Jane Goodall sitting together on the end of a jetty watching the fireflies, gazing at the lazy flow of the river, and sipping brandy from a flask she had brought. She told me having an evening drink was a tradition she and her mother, Vanne, started in Africa and perhaps one of the reasons her mother lived to be so old.

Near the end of the conference, Minister Sudarman and Director General Joop Ave came from Jakarta to the Rimba Lodge to ceremoniously hear our documented findings and receive our official proclamation, which was signed and enshrined at the Rimba Lodge. After the conference was over and the high officials returned to Jakarta, I left Tanjung Puting with the remaining organizers, exhausted and confused by the sudden ending. With all the follow-up and clean-up ahead of me, I had no intention of conducting, much less overseeing, another conference any time soon.

But just seven years later, however, I was asked to organize the third Great Apes of the World Conference in Kuching, Malaysia. It was another challenging undertaking that had financial support by the Malaysian Tourism department as well as by OFI. Unlike the Indonesian government, the Malaysians had a budget to promote conferences such as this. Malaysia Airlines agreed to fly me and two other OFI representatives to Malaysia to meet with officials and determine possible venues. I chose Rod Briggs and John Pearson to accompany me, two people I trusted for their longtime support of OFI and their abilities to negotiate and raise funds.

While we were being "wined and dined" by the hotel managers during our visit, our discussions with James Masing, Minister of Tourism, made me uneasy. Like with our Indonesian government hosts, the Malaysians were suspicious of foreign scientists and academics who were not afraid to speak their mind. Masing, who was outwardly congenial and gracious, wanted me to make sure there would be no criticism of the Sarawak government by the attendees, especially regarding development projects, such as the controversial Bakun Dam, and government responses to local protests over land rights that were regularly in the news. I felt uncomfortable being put on the spot. I couldn't guarantee him anything, but what was I to say? Of course I told him I would do my best to mitigate any such criticism by our attendees.

After I returned to Los Angeles, I had to round up experts and put together the agenda for the event scheduled for late 1998, but what I remember most about preparing for this conference was that Jane Goodall declined to attend. Despite my repeated efforts to get her to change her mind, she wouldn't relent and apologized to me for her decision that was based purely on irrational feelings linked to the violence and social unrest in the nearby country of Indonesia following the fall of President Soeharto from office in 1997. Her decision seemed to impact other chimpanzee experts, many of whom also declined to come to Sarawak.

However, the conference was held from July 3 to 6, 1998, and it was well attended by academics and laypeople alike, showcasing Malaysia's culture and natural beauty. The theme of the conference, "Securing Great Ape Survival into the Next Millennium", was referenced and expanded upon by Sarawak's Tourism Minister, James Masing, in his opening address as well as his plea to the attendees to "take time after the conference to discover more of Sarawak." Numerous papers on all the great apes were presented, panel sessions were held, commitments and agreements were hammered out by the Action Planning Committee, and sponsored luncheons brought the attendees together to socialize and forge new partnerships and projects. Side trips and post-conference ecotours were commonly arranged, and to my knowledge, no one said anything publicly critical about the Sarawak government, but the event as a whole put me in a pressure cooker: I had to manage many things, from the needs and concerns of over 100 attendees, to technical emergencies during the breakout sessions, all while ensuring Galdikas was always at the right location for her to make presentations or meet with officials for public statements.

Even the special invitation for my wife and I to be chauffeured to the Chief Minister's residence for a special party was a stressful aspect of my running the event, not to deny the honor. Datuk Abdul Taib Mahmud was a controversial ruler of the resource rich Malaysian state, who had been in power as Chief Minister since 1981, and used his position and authority to develop Sarawak. According to his critics, he amassed a fortune at the expense of the forests and human rights. For the record, I found him and his Polish born wife, Laila, to be warm and quite charming as they celebrated their adult daughter's birthday with their Canadian-born son-in-law, though their home was quite opulent. Interestingly, in his opening dinner speech, he compared his ethnically diverse family to the multicolored rivers of Sarawak sometimes blending into each other as they flowed to the sea.

Regardless, during dinner, I committed what I have come to realize was a serious faux pas. Sitting right next to him, I asked, "Datuk Taib, how long do you plan on being Chief Minister?" I immediately felt embarrassed, for I had some sense of what I had just done, but he looked at me pondering the question for a moment then smiled. He said he was ready to step down, but he was still looking for the right person to replace him, though I suspected this was a canned response that he had said many times over the years, even then. It was a stupid question. I regret it to this day.

Still despite all that was going on to showcase the plight of the various species of great apes, rainforests around and sometimes within protected areas were being illegally cleared in several countries. While lip service was being paid to the orangutan, the situation was like a bleeding patient whose hemorrhagic fever was treated by doctors arguing over the best type of Band-Aids to stop the bleeding.

Clearly, something important was missing from the work that had been done for so long by so many organizations, government and non-government. From my perspective, it required a long-term investment in changing attitudes, values, and culture. Ignorance, indifference, fear, apathy, pride, and greed were the fundamental causes. Education was the key to addressing the root causes to create positive change, but I knew OFI was not going to invest enough in educating the Indonesian public about the plight of orangutans, because most of its funding was being spent on food, medicine, and local caregivers for the hundreds of orphaned orangutans being managed at Camp Leakey, the other release areas, the new facility, and at the baby school near Galdikas's home in Pasir Panjang. There would simply not be enough to go around.

Orang Utan Republik

Orangutan males go through a unique transformation between sub-adulthood and full adulthood (Maggioncalda, 1999). While traveling within the forest as a sub-adult, they appear from a distance to be another female. Fully adult males will not bother to chase them away. They are effectively wearing female clothing and avoiding confrontation with the resident cheek-padder. Females do not find them sexually attractive, so the sub-adults forcibly mate with adult female orangutans. Sub-adult or unflanged males will stay that way and employ that sexual strategy as long as the sound of the resident adult male's long call is heard or the sub-adult perceives the presence of the adult male. Testosterone is suppressed, even when the male reaches twenty years or older.

If during his journey away from the resident male, the sight, sounds, and scents of the adult male diminish to a level where the sub-adult no longer perceives the threat or presence of the adult male, something amazing happens. The pituitary goes into action, and a secondary surge of testosterone starts to flow. Like Marvel Universe's Bruce Banner, the male orangutan changes into the Hulk over a period of several months. Orangutan males almost double in size, grow out their characteristic cheek pads and throat pouch, and proudly give the signature "long call" to announce their presence and in the evening communicating the direction they intend to travel the following day (van Schaik, et al., 2013). This amazing physical transformation is permanent. Calming down won't cause the body to revert back to the old cross-dressing days. Those days are over.

Such as it was for me. Eighteen years was enough to see what roadblocks we were not going to overcome, and staying with OFI was negatively impacting my relationship with my wife. Over the years, Inggriani, my wife, had been gracious to Galdikas by occasionally babysitting her daughter, hosting her husband and students from Jakarta at our home, and tolerating my long hours away from my family life to serve Galdikas and the organization. But Inggriani was not a shy and demure Asian woman. When it became too much for her, she told Galdikas not to call me in the middle of the night to chat for hours, and she asked pointed questions to Galdikas about how the foundation funds were being used. Galdikas, in a private lunchtime meeting, had said some hurtful and unforgivable things to Inggriani, and Inggriani felt that as long as I was with OFI, I was supporting the "other woman." I was also dissatisfied as the number two person in an organization that was not doing enough to address the underlying cause for all the orangutan killings. Like the restless sub-adult male orangutan, I felt my passion to serve the cause, to actually make a difference, was being suppressed. So, in November 2004, during the annual meeting of OFI, I initiated a major shakeup. I, along with several other generous and active board members, announced our resignations. Each of us had our own reasons. It was a shocking moment for President Galdikas, and there was no turning back. Not even the offer of the presidency by one of the remaining board members was enough to keep me in the shadow of Galdikas. Like the sub-adult male, I needed separation from the dominant authority and the organization we both conceived and developed. The orangutans needed that too, an organization to stop the cycle, not just pick up after it. OFI was incapable of doing this, as the money Inggriani and I had raised for education programs in OFI was redirected by the board to be used to feed the babies pouring into the Care Center. When I resigned, there was only $1,000 earmarked for education, only a single thousand to help stop future babies from having their mother's murdered before their eyes.

The Orang Utan Republik Education Initiative (OUREI) was my solution. From my experience with OFI, I knew a lot about start-ups, and I knew I could not afford to get bogged down with administration, so I reached out to the Social and Environmental Entrepreneurs (SEE), a 501c3 nonprofit sponsor for both funding and administration assistance. For a nominal administrative fee, we hit the ground running.

Our first act was to operate a handicrafts booth at the Sunday Farmer's Market in Santa Monica. Perhaps this sounds like a small step, which it was, but it was nonetheless important. It was a very popular tourist destination, so it was a good way to directly interact and educate the public from across the world. We did this for five years, selling the sustainable handicrafts sourced from women's collectives in Indonesia under our provocative name, Orang Utan Republik. It was a labor of love to put on these weekly outreach events, and over time, volunteers made the effort easier and effective.

Of course, even though we had an audience of mainly westside shoppers, we also had to educate the local Indonesian community, something we could hardly do from a booth in the crowded Santa Monica Farmer's Market. So, while we worked on increasing our influence stateside, we reached out to an influential Indonesian personality to help us, Angelina Sondakh, a former Miss Indonesia and newly elected legislator. This was a happy accident, as we were attending a public gathering with various newly elected Indonesian legislators at the Indonesian Consulate in Los Angeles, so we could hardly turn such serendipity away. Through our conversation, Ms. Sondakh turned out to have a true love of nature and had already been an ambassador for the spectral tarsier, a diminutive primate found in the forests of Ms. Sondakh's native island of Sulawesi. After my wife explained our program to her, she asked us to visit her in Jakarta the next time we visited Indonesia. Naturally, there was little question about whether to accept her offer, so on our following trip to Jakarta on July 11, 2005, we went to her office at the top of the Parliament building and presented her with a specially prepared certificate appointing her as our ambassador. She accepted our appointment, and thus we began planning our first widespread initiative to educate the Indonesian populace, Orangutan Caring Week. This, unfortunately, was not an easy event to orchestrate, because it was being done at the national level and that necessitated significant coordination and support from the Indonesian bureaucracy.

Despite these struggles and with Angelina's help, we got the Minister of Forestry to support the idea and get it scheduled for launch at the Parliament Building the following November. Then it was time to announce it globally. I invited Indonesian and Western orangutan researchers and conservationists who I knew to join us at the press conference. Print, television, and online news services covered the event. The minister mentioned the government's commitment to conserving forests and orangutan populations, but his government tacitly endorsed unsustainable agriculture and the illegal palm oil operations that were destroying habitat and killing orangutans.

As I stood with others in front of the cameras and reporters seeking comments, I was nervous about our messaging. The challenge of announcing what was really happening to the orangutans was left to the conservationists who needed to artfully articulate the problems still affecting forests and orangutans without insulting the Indonesian government or their policies. To their credit, the conservationists, myself included, deftly navigated the fine line between addressing the plight of the species and promoting positive actions, enough so that I was not embarrassed at least.

Over the week, parliament members attended the outreach events in the downstairs halls learning more about the issues and what was being done by the various groups. Did these decision makers actually care more about orangutans by the end of the week? Well, at the very least, they became more aware of the issues, especially the international concern being expressed. Being able to reach an influential audience, some of whom probably owned orangutans or were invested in timber and palm oil companies, made sense to us. I was satisfied by the turnout and the news coverage. The press featured stories about orangutans and their plight almost every day. Equally important, the event was improving the level of understanding about the issues among the Indonesian people who were exposed to more press about orangutans that week than what was covered by the media outlets during the prior year.

Following the inaugural Orangutan Caring Week in Indonesia, high school and college students contacted Angelina's office, so to harness their interest, the Orangutan Caring Club was established. I was glad to hear that meetings were held at Angelina's penthouse office to organize the young people. School visits and outreach activities were prepared. Farther away, young people in Medan, Sumatra also started an Orangutan Caring Club.

While the Jakarta Orangutan Caring Club had Angelina's celebrity status to promote the conservation message, the Caring Club in Medan could take students to the orangutan viewing area in the Bukit Lawang region of the Mount Leuser National Park. This was an area that had been a rehabilitation station, like Camp Leakey, but was turned into a place for eco-tourists to watch the descendants of ex-captive orangutans come to the feeding station.

As I sat comfortably back in my office in Santa Monica pondering over the email I received from Angelina about the progress, I was elated our initial plans were unfolding through Indonesian engagement, but I knew I had to step up and do more to accelerate the process. I wired funds to Angelina's senior assistant, Ridhwan Effendi, to help fund the Caring Club's operations.

I also wanted OUREI to promote conferences as a way to share information among various organizations about important issues impacting critically endangered Sumatran orangutans. While we could have examined eco-tourism or palm oil issues, I asked respected orangutan researcher and conservationist, Dr. Ian Singleton, in 2005 what he thought would be a relevant and important topic. Having recently attended numerous mind-numbing meetings, Ian said that we needed a conference specifically addressing the killing of orangutans in Sumatra.

I wholeheartedly agreed to take on the responsibility and embarked on the journey to secure the necessary funding for the "Sumatran Orangutan Education Conference, Workshop, and Summit" (CWS). Fortunately, my efforts bore fruit as I successfully obtained matching funding from the U.S. Fish and Wildlife Service through their esteemed Great Apes Conservation Fund.

However, the road ahead was not without its obstacles. Before diving into the logistics and execution of the CWS, I had to navigate the challenges of fundraising, planning, and ultimately holding the event. Surprisingly, raising money proved to be the least of my concerns. It was the intricacies of garnering local support and managing the politics among various organizations, each with their own agendas and opinions, that presented the greatest hurdles.

I vividly recall the uncomfortable planning meetings held in Medan. As I sat among the hardcore Indonesian environmentalist leaders, I couldn't help but feel the tension in the room. Their critical gaze scrutinized every aspect of our choices, and they threatened to withdraw their support over disagreements regarding the guest list and who we intended to honor at the CWS.

In those moments, I realized the weight of the task I had undertaken. Balancing the desires and expectations of these influential figures while staying true to the vision and purpose of the event required delicate diplomacy. I had to show them I wasn't a pushy Westerner but a partner in conservation seeking their input and advice. It was a delicate dance, where compromise and tact became my allies.

These internal challenges, though arduous and at times disheartening, ultimately served as a reminder of the shared commitment we held towards our cause. The "Sumatran Orangutan Education Conference, Workshop, and Summit" became more than just an event; it became a platform for bridging gaps, fostering collaboration, and collectively working towards a brighter future for these remarkable creatures.

A pre-workshop to the event was held on November 9, 2006, in Medan to jumpstart the process while the conference portion and main workshop of the CWS was held the following week at a hotel in the resort city of Berastagi from November 15 & 16. I gave one of the opening speeches entitled, "saving a species through education" following the initial presentation on the "legal aspects of biodiversity protection" by the director for biodiversity conservation for Indonesia. Local and foreign researchers, conservationists, wildlife managers, and education specialists made presentations in their native language to illustrate the current challenges facing orangutan conservation as well as possible solutions for their long-term survival. The culmination of our collected efforts was showcased at the summit on November 17 in Medan as our results and recommendations were unveiled. One of the highlights was the presentation of the meticulously titled "Declaration and Commitment of the Sumatran Orangutan Education Conference, Workshop, and Summit of 2006 for Saving the Species through Education and Outreach." This document, signed by over one hundred attendees, served as a powerful symbol of our shared dedication to orangutan conservation.

The declaration encompassed various critical aspects related to the plight of the orangutan, including acknowledging the existing laws protecting the species and recognizing the urgent need for widespread education. It solidified our commitment to deliver the recommended curricula in the following year. This commitment had been an integral part of the grant proposal I had labored over and submitted to the U.S. Fish and Wildlife Service, which would ultimately provide the funds required to support our initiatives.

Unfortunately, despite the successes of our activities in Indonesia, I grew increasingly frustrated that some people, especially prospective donors, weren't taking us seriously working under Social and Environmental Entrepreneurs' administrative umbrella. We were considered a project, not a real nonprofit organization. That changed in 2007, when OUREI became the Orang Utan Republik Foundation (OURF), a 501(c)(3) organization with its own board of directors and officers. We also formed a legal nonprofit organization in Indonesia, OUREI Indonesia, and during the first several years of the organization, we managed the Orangutan Caring Clubs and supported the motivated conservation educators in Jakarta and Medan with funding from OURF. We also created and funded a unique initiative called the Orangutan Caring Scholarship (OCS) program implemented by local orangutan NGOs to provide tuition-based support for university undergraduates from the five orangutan-range provinces in Indonesia. The degree programs being funded have been mainly in biology, forestry and veterinary science, all positioned to nurture future orangutan conservationists and advocates. The accomplishments of these programs have underscored the importance of reliance and trust among conservation organizations.

For conservation efforts to be understood, it is of utmost importance to acknowledge the glaring disparity in funding between organizations like OURF and other environmental NGOs, in comparison to the vast financial resources allocated by big businesses involved in the destructive dismantling of rainforests for estate plantations, mines, hydroelectric projects, and other forms of development that primarily serve the interests of their shareholders.

Tragically, the consequences of this overwhelming difference in resources have been devastating. Over the past forty years, we have witnessed the loss of more than half of the world's species, a stark reality documented by the World Wildlife Fund in 2018. Even almost a decade ago, experts were already proclaiming, with good reason, that we are in the midst of a sixth mass extinction event also known as the Anthropocene Mass Extinction with extinction rates 100 to 1,000 times the prehistoric background rates (De Vos, et al., 2015). Exploitation, agriculture, and land conversion have all played significant roles in this harrowing decline.

However, for those of us who have dedicated our lives to the cause of conservation, the battle is worth every ounce of effort exerted, even in the face of such oppressive circumstances. Hope remains ever-present, although we continually wonder when key global leaders and decision-makers will finally prioritize environmental and existential issues over the traditional corporate focus on short-term profits. The U.N. Sustainable Development Goals, as outlined by Griggs , et al. in 2013, represent a positive step in the right direction. They provided a framework that addresses the urgent need for action, that unfortunately few have taken. Too many do not recognize that it is not only the lives of great apes that are at stake, but also the futures of our children and grandchildren, and their little dogs too.

Creating truly protected areas for orangutans and the biodiversity of the planet remains uncertain when governments, like Indonesia, have few protected areas and even less enforcement. Fueling the unregulated global markets leads to encroachments by impoverished farmers or greedy entrepreneurs who engage in logging, oil palm cultivation, and clearing of native rainforest trees for agriculture even within national parks. In the case of Indonesia, forest lands under the jurisdiction of the Department of Agriculture are frequently earmarked for conversion, despite any potential legal restrictions on clearing forests, which is why it is so important that conservationists work together.

One quite promising solution to be had by joining forces has emerged in recent years: the establishment of privately managed Forest Concessions for conservation. While the process is lengthy and costly in a country like Indonesia, a granted license empowers the managing company to defend the integrity of the forest and, in turn, bestows a degree of sovereignty upon whomever they wish, say, the orangutans and other species residing within the concession borders. This approach aligns with the original vision of an Orang Utan Republik, wherein humans act as stewards and advocates for great apes.

This said, preserving the existing forests where wild orangutans thrive remains the most cost-effective means of ensuring their long-term survival in a conservational sense, as emphasized by Santika , et al. in 2022. Each wild population has developed its unique proto-culture within its specific habitat, and it would be ethically unacceptable to jeopardize these cultures by relocating different groups solely for political expediency. Just as no human wants to be uprooted from their homeland, we must stand up for the orangutan individuals who lack the ability to voice their concerns or fight for their rights.

While protecting and expanding forest habitats and implementing Forest Concessions are worthy endeavors, the amount of funding we would need to do so is in the millions. Why millions of dollars? Because without such funding, the Indonesian government, and frankly many other governments as well, will continue to receive substantial fees from logging companies or palm oil plantations operating within these concessions for thirty years or longer, much less the unpunished financial incentives for invasions into the orangutan forests by local populations. With funding from a competing source, the government can be made to take enforcement actions against those who destroy or degrade protected forests and to provide greater legal protection to current orangutan populations and their habitats outside of protected areas.

The disparity is monumental, not insurmountable.

Gallery Three

1. Jimmy, the young orangutan, held by his previous owner/adoptive parent.

2. Rescued juvenile and early adolescent orangutans being held in a secure holding facility.

3. A group of ex-captive orangutans on the boardwalk at Camp Leakey, all victims of the illegal pet trade.

4. An afternoon seining fish in a seasonal lake near Camp Leakey as part of my self-funded post-doctoral study of the Sekonyer River in mid-to-late 1986.

5. Lawyer John Beal, Birute Galdikas, and I holding a phone meeting during the formative stages of OFI.

6. Galdikas and I working on a newsletter article at the OFI office.

7. With volunteers at an OFI event during the early days of the Foundation.

8. Group of volunteers including Liz Varnhagen and my parents preparing OFI newsletters for mass mailing at the OFI office.

9. During my trip to Taiwan meeting naturalist Charles Shuttleworth and Marcus Phipps (right).

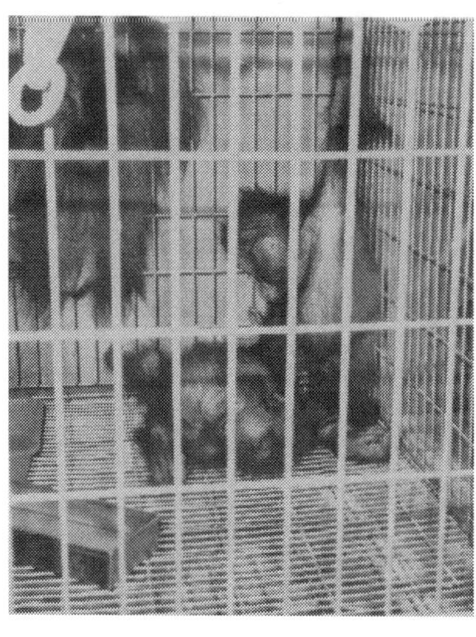

10. Orangutans babies being sold in a Taipei pet store in the 1990s.

11. An orangutan being used as a prop at a store in "Snake Alley" to attract customers.

12. Speaking to students about orangutan conservation in a school in Taipei during my visit.

13. Sitting in the transport bus in front of the Presidential Palace with my wife, Inggriani, besides me and Dr. Jane Goodall in front.

14. Official photograph of shaking the hand of President Soeharto during the opening ceremony of the Second Great Apes of the World Conference.

15. Official photographs of attendees to the opening of the Second Great Apes of the World Conference held at the Presidential Palace in Jakarta, Indonesia. President Soeharto and key ministers (lower left).

16. Official group photographs of attendees to the Third Great Apes of the World Conference held in Kuching, Sarawak, Malaysia.

17. With the Chief Minister of Sarawak and Birute Galdikas during the opening ceremony.

18. Speaking briefly with Chief Minister Datuk Taib during a break at the Great Ape Conference.

19. Standing with some Conference attendees including Peter Singer, Malaysian official, Birute Galdikas, Ian Redmond, Chief Minister Taib, and Corazon from Malaysia Airlines .

20. My wife, Inggriani, and I interviewed by Voice of America Indonesia at Santa Monica Farmer's Market during the inception of Orang Utan Republik.

21. With Dr. Ian Singleton, OURF Ambassador Angelina Sondakh and Forestry Minister MS Kaban to formally announce Orangutan Caring Week at the Parliament Building in Jakarta.

22. Findings of the Sumatran Orangutan Education Conference, Workshop, and Summit are announced while key participants and supporters stand behind.

23. Some of the attendees to the conference portion of the Sumatran Orangutan Education Conference, Workshop, and Summit.

24. Syarifah Lia Andriati, the inaugural recipient of the Orangutan Caring Scholarship (OCS).

25. Some of the OCS recipients from N. Sumatra and Aceh during an award presentation.

26. In 2021, the Center for Orangutan Protection joined forces with OURF as the final NGO partner to launch the East Borneo Orangutan Caring Scholarship program.

27. Delivering an engaging presentation to elementary school students in Bukit Lawang as part of the OURF-funded Mobile Education and Conservation Program (2010-2019).

28. OURF-funded Community Education and Conservation Program staff empowering village women through technical training to produce organic fertilizer, fostering livelihood enhancements.

29. Orangutan person Sandra languishing alone in her enclosure at the Buenos Aires Zoo.

30. Sandra peering out the glass portion of her enclosure at the visitors to the Buenos Aires Zoo.

31. Sandra was transferred to the Center for Great Apes sanctuary in Florida in November 2019 where she is thriving with other orangutans. While she lost her "personhood" status, she has gained a friendship with Jethro.

32. Part of my journey has included celebrating at our Pongo Environmental Award events where we honor environmental achievement and raise funds for OURF.

33. In 2018, we held our Pongo Awards at an art gallery in Santa Monica where supporters could meet and schmooze outdoors before the award program inside.

34. In 2019, we joined forces with The Orangutan Project for our Pongo Awards, coinciding with a gala and book launch for Leif Cocks in Culver City, CA.

35. In 2021, a gala event took place at the Indonesian Consulate in Los Angeles.

36. Dr. Jane Goodall graciously accepting a Pongo Environmental Award in 2015.

Orangutan Rights in Action

In many ways, this section offers a summary of orangutan intelligence, social behavior, emotional life, and personhood through the account of Sandra and demonstrates a real-life application in the fight for orangutan personhood, rights, and sovereignty.

Sandra's Story

Sandra sat quietly and alone in her enclosure – a metal and concrete structure that ensured she could not leave its confines and wander toward the other structures which she occasionally gazed upon. With a blanket on her head, she lay out on her belly and took her long fingers to slowly break up the straw that was given to her to play and nest in. This was the life of Sandra, an orangutan. Yet for a group of animal rights lawyers in the city of Buenos Aires, Argentina, her life of incarceration at the city zoo was a clear case of Sandra suffering. This assessment of suffering was not a statement made by Sandra to the lawyers. They inferred her suffering and took legal action to have Sandra released on the grounds of habeas corpus. This is a complex story that I played a small part in as an expert witness on May 13, 2015, in a courtroom in Argentina via Skype.

Sandra's story began when she was born at the Rostock Zoo in Germany on Valentine's Day, 1986, the child of Bornean and Sumatran orangutan parents and given the name Marisa by the zoo staff. Marisa was transferred to several zoos in Germany before being sent to

Buenos Aires, Argentina on September 17, 1993, where her name was changed to Sandra.

At the Buenos Aires Zoo, Sandra lived in a sterile concrete and steel bar cage with an outdoor area the size of a basketball court. From the age of seven, this was the place Sandra learned to call home. She was thus an institutionalized orangutan who interacted with zoo staff and watched the zoo visitors from behind a glass wall or from the outdoor area. Like most orangutans, Sandra had the tendency to put cloth, burlap sacks, or other material on her head. This behavior seems to comfort orangutans as well as provide protection from the elements.

At thirteen years of age, Sandra reportedly gave birth to a son, Gembira ("Happy" in Indonesian) on March 2, 1999. It is unclear who fathered the child, but Sandra experienced one of her first major disappointments when she was separated from her son in 2007, and taken to the Cordoba Zoo seven hundred kilometers away to breed with the orangutan named Max, an orangutan she reportedly spent time with at the Buenos Aires Zoo years earlier. It is also unclear if she ever saw her son again, for Gembira was sent to the Xixiakou Wild Animal Park in Rongcheng, China in 2008.

It should be noted, as mentioned elsewhere in these pages, that in the wild the close bond between mother and offspring would have been broken at around this age; however, Sandra's relationship with Gembira was more than that of mother/son, for Gembira was also Sandra's cage mate and someone of her own species with whom she could choose to interact with. Now the zoos were trying to get her to breed with the orangutan Max at the Cordoba Zoo and Sandra didn't want any part of it. According to veterinarian Dr. Hector Ferrari's June 23, 2015, report to the court, "As from the moment she got there, she never wanted to go close to the male and always slept outside. Despite the fact she was with a familiar animal, she was not able to use the whole space and never agreed to share the internal area with the male, although Max was never aggressive. Sandra endured rain and some snowfall in the outdoor area." This suggests that Sandra's prior familiarity with Max was not enough for her to find him of sexual interest. Indeed, she tolerated harsh weather conditions outside to actively avoid being near Max. In the wild, females that are not proceptive and still with the offspring will avoid contact with adult male orangutans. We do not know what took place between the two of them in their early years or the hormonal condition of Sandra at the time, but it is clear she had a choice in the matter and probably was still psychologically attached to her son. After this failed effort, Sandra was returned to the Buenos Aires Zoo. It is unclear if her son had been transferred to China by that time.

The legal team from the Association of Officers and Lawyers for the Rights of Animals (AFADA) knew about the deplorable conditions at the zoo and of Sandra's situation. Indeed, one hundred nineteen animals had reportedly died prematurely in the Buenos Aires Zoo over its one hundred forty-year history. Led by the legal team of Pablo Buompadre and Gil Domingo, AFADA, since early 2014, repeatedly appealed to the court system in Argentina to free Sandra from the zoo in order to relocate her to a sanctuary under a writ of habeas corpus. Each time the courts denied Sandra would be eligible under said writ but have affirmed her rights for protection under the laws of Argentina protecting animals and effectively giving her "non-human person" status.

A legal ruling in a criminal appeals court on December 18, 2014, led to a flurry of news articles stating that Sandra had received the right to life, liberty, and freedom from harm (Román, 2015). AFADA was claiming Sandra would be released and relocated to a sanctuary in short order. The ruling by the judges Ledesma, David, and Skolar recognized "the animal as a subject of rights, because non-human beings (animals) are entitled to rights, and therefore their protection is required by the corresponding jurisprudence" under Argentinian animal protection law. AFADA interpreted this ruling as the court giving Sandra "non-human personhood" status. Of course, the Buenos Aires Zoo did not agree with the notion that Sandra was going to be liberated no matter what was being stated in the press.

Enter Judge Elena Liberatori of the fourth court on Contentious Administrative and Tax Matters who in early 2015 agreed to adjudicate AFADA's latest appeal for a full hearing regarding Sandra's freedom. This legal precedent hit the press and was published internationally as groundbreaking by giving Sandra non-human person status in a court of law. In fact, the judge's agreement was mistranslated by the press. Instead of habeas corpus, whose legal history dates back from before the Magna Carta, the judge was treating the case as a "writ of amparo," another legal mechanism more commonly used in Spanish speaking countries intended to protect all rights that are not protected specifically. Thus, Sandra was indeed being considered a non-human person in Argentina. She would get her day in court, not by taking the stand on her own, but through representation by others on her behalf.

This was historic and I was honored to have been asked to be the first of three orangutan "experts" to advise the court about orangutans and recommendations for Sandra. The three of us, Leif Cocks, Shawn Thompson, and I, formed a committee to determine what lines of testimony and statements to make before the court via Skype. We certainly wanted to provide the Judge with scientific and observational evidence supporting the relocation of Sandra to an appropriate sanctuary where she could live out her life in dignity and in ways that would express her orangutan potential. At the very least, we wanted to make statements that would improve Sandra's current situation.

Cocks had spent decades as a zookeeper and zoo supervisor for the orangutans at the Perth Zoo in Australia. He conducted research on the housing and management of orangutans over the years and was successful in preparing and returning a captive orangutan named Tamara to life in the Sumatran wild. He is also the president of the largest orangutan advocacy organization, The Orangutan Project (Cocks, 2016).

While Cocks and I have had significant personal hands-on experience with orangutans, Thompson has long studied orangutan issues as a writer (2010), written about human incarceration (2002), and is supportive of great ape rights. Thompson (2019) discussed Sandra's case in a paper that examined the legal principle of autonomy and scientific assessments of great ape cognitive abilities that would be of value for lawyers like Steven Wise to support evidence of autonomy in the United States courtroom.

My testimony to the court came on the morning of May 13, 2015, in a Skype video-conference call with Judge Elena Amanda Liberatori and a dozen others including members of Sandra's legal defense team, city officials, zoo staff and a translator. I had prepared notes for my statements, as I didn't want to ramble on with the limited time I had to represent the expert team on Sandra's behalf.

After introducing myself, my background, and my experience with great apes, I mentioned that we had not been given a report issued by the Buenos Aires Zoo about Sandra, a report that would have enabled our team to better address Sandra's situation. I also pointed out that no other independent orangutan expert had a chance to observe Sandra to assess her behavioral and mental health. Only zoo staff and the local university zoologist had observed Sandra's behavior in the context of the concerns raised by AFADA. We had no independent assessment of Sandra to determine if she were suffering and, if so, the degree to which she was in emotional or physical distress. For example, we had no knowledge if Sandra exhibited any type of stereotypic behavior (e.g., repetitious rocking, banging her head, pulling her hair out, etc.).

In the absence of being able to consider and compare Sandra with other orangutans, I continued by letting the court have a better understanding of the behavior of wild orangutans; free-ranging, ex-captive orangutans; and captive, institutionalized orangutans, especially from the adult female perspective. I first presented the concept of an ethogram of a wild orangutan, mentioning that they spend over 60% of their day feeding or searching for food. It was important to let the court know that such a simple activity budget would allow us to understand how Sandra would compare to her wild orangutan peers. According to the veterinarian present, no ethogram of Sandra was ever constructed. I then discussed basic orangutan behavior, emphasizing the mother's strong social bond to her offspring while the pair travels from food source to food source during the course of the day. Orangutans are mentally stimulated as they travel safely through the three-dimensional forest world in pursuit of scattered ripe and nutritious fruit. I mentioned the long inter-birth interval and avoidance of social relations with adult males for many years. Self-contained and confident without depending on a group leader, the mother orangutan with her dependent offspring focus on finding enough high-quality food to avoid starvation and to sequester fat reserves needed to support future offspring.

I explained to the court that formerly captive orangutans can learn to live in the wild or within a managed nature reserve as free-ranging individuals. Younger orangutans must spend years in learning and practicing how to climb, navigate in trees, build sleeping nests, and identify and open different foods. This has been the case at a variety of centers in Sumatra and Borneo, including the location where I spent years in Central Kalimantan.

I emphasized that free-ranging orangutans have the choice to move freely and interact with others of their kind as well as with humans. They are much more sociable than their wild cousins. They stimulate their own minds, even when they are provisioned, by foraging in the nearby forest, or breaking into buildings, playing with other orangutans, and many other self-directed activities. Their destructive nature within the camp setting is a healthy outlet for their natural foraging behavior. Yet, too many individuals restricted to a confined area can destroy the nascent forest before it can regenerate. Incidentally, this is an important consideration in orangutan conservation efforts.

Finally, I asked the court to consider the captive, institutionalized orangutan. Born into captivity, she does not know what she has missed from living in the rainforest. She likely was separated from her mother who was almost certainly a captive individual who never learned proper maternal behavior and may have had her offspring removed because of this, causing stress. She has lived in a solitary situation for many years. She is fed by staff and may have no incentive to travel for food within her environment (i.e., limited or no behavioral enrichment or exercise). Her life is repetitive and boring. She conceivably "resents" how she cannot leave the area like her human caregivers.

I explained to the court my basic contention that orangutans (and other sentient animals) suffer in captivity because important psychological, recreational, and emotional needs are not met. My personal opinion was that more attention should be devoted to providing a higher standard of care to address their needs, recognizing that we cannot necessarily release these beings into the wild for ethical and practical reasons.

What needs should be considered to improve the status of Sandra the orangutan to reduce or avoid her suffering? I provided four general categories based on the team's discussions: 1. Need for space and physical movement; 2. Need for mental stimulation; 3. Need for freedom and choice; 4. Need for the choice to be social or alone. For each need, I provided supporting testimony based on our team's understanding and personal observations. For example, in discussing the need for space and physical movement, the vertical dimension in enclosures is an important consideration for a species that normally live an arboreal life. Likewise, the need to be mentally stimulated in captive situations is as important as physical exercise for a great ape whose brain has evolved for individual problem-solving. The need for freedom and choice is based on the acceptance that Sandra and other captive great apes are sentient and self-aware of their incarceration and suffer as they ponder over the inequity of their condition relative to their caregivers. Providing them choice is vital for their well-being as it gives them a sense of control and stimulation in their lives. Finally, the special need for choice in being social or alone for Sandra respects her desire to socially interact, or not, and gives her a say in the matter. Addressing such a need recognizes the species' natural predisposition to choose a solitary lifestyle in the wild depending on circumstances such as having to seek food when and where it is limited or avoiding threatening individuals.

My testimony concluded by providing the court with the recommendations from our expert team which would include sending Leif Cocks, our captive management expert, to evaluate Sandra and her condition and to consider potential facilities that would better serve her.

Such a facility where Sandra could be relocated would be based on assessments of the various potential places that could meet Sandra's needs for space, sociality/privacy, freedom, choice, and mental stimulation. That facility would also have a veterinarian specializing in orangutans. We also recommended that Sandra not be sent back to the wild, for she would be unable to adjust to such a life without a significant amount of training, something Sandra might not be able to achieve given her experience as an institutionalized captive. Additionally, we would not want Sandra to suffer in quarantine if it is determined she would be best placed in a facility outside Argentina. Quarantine would be needed if she entered a new country. Judge Liberatori asked me if it would be possible to adjust the current enclosure at the zoo to improve life for Sandra. I answered by saying that whatever remedy takes place, it should be a qualitative improvement not a slight adjustment. I added I was there to represent Sandra, not just to recommend finding a quick solution. To give her a say in her future, our team recommended that Sandra be offered some options in the selection of her accommodation to the extent that her choices would reflect her preferences. Finally, we strongly recommended that Sandra's rights as a non-human person and her welfare dominate the decision, not costs.

I answered questions from the panel in court about my experience with orangutans in captivity and in Kalimantan, facts about orangutans, Sandra's sentience, and took notice of a smiling Judge Liberatori when I spoke about my relationship with Princess, the free-ranging juvenile orangutan I raised as my daughter while learning how to sign. I was asked about my recommendations for Sandra before her being relocated, in response to which I reiterated the need for behavioral enrichment to stimulate her mind. I was also pleased to hear that the zoo was planning on showing Sandra photographs of enrichment items for her to make a choice of the actual item while the court was deciding on Sandra's future location. It seemed the zoo and the courts understood how important it was to address Sandra's mental needs and to alleviate boredom. When the testimony was over, I felt satisfied that I was able to be an advocate for Sandra and her future. If we don't speak on behalf of orangutans, who will?

In the weeks thereafter, Shawn Thompson and Leif Cocks also testified, emphasizing other aspects of orangutan behavior and biology, Sandra's autonomy, Sandra's suffering in captivity, and captive management options that would address her rights as well as our recommendations. After presenting the Judge with our final report, including recommendations regarding Sandra's future, we thanked Judge Elena Liberatori in our conclusion "for her sincerity and willingness to hear and consider our recommendations in the difficult decision she has to make."

Following our testimony, two university consultants in veterinary science for the Buenos Aires Zoo, in late May 2015, offered a set of improvements to Sandra's enclosure, some of which would allow for softer surfaces and behavioral enrichment activities including novel items and interaction with staff, permitting a level of "human-animal bonding." Included were recommendations for giving choice to Sandra for where she could sleep or when she would be able to engage with caregivers. The zoo was clearly trying to mitigate our recommendations which advocated that Sandra be relocated to a sanctuary that would address her needs. While Sandra's situation might be ameliorated by such improvements, they did not advance AFADA's efforts to take Sandra's non-human person status as an avenue for her release from incarceration. The city of Buenos Aires was also asserting its domain of possession by criticizing efforts to transfer Sandra to another institution. Sandra's best interest seemed secondary to local pride.

On October 21, 2015, Judge Elena Liberatori (2015) issued her final decision on Sandra's case: AFADA vs. the government of the City of Buenos Aires. The judge affirmed Sandra's non-human person status and stated that, "Sandra has the right to enjoy the highest quality of life possible to her particular and individual situation, tending to avoid any kind of suffering that could be generated by the interference of humans in her life." While not closing the door on Sandra's transfer to a sanctuary, she would be staying at the zoo for the time being. In her thirteen-page ruling, the judge laid out the argument brought before the court including the recognition of Sandra's situation, her sentient qualities, and presumed suffering, citing our expert team's contribution including our testimony and final recommendations on October 5, 2015, the jurisdiction of the city, and other facts, testimony, and legal opinion as is typically written into a legal decision by the court. Judge Liberatori then resolved to approve the action of protection submitted under the following terms: "To recognize the orangutan Sandra as a subject of law, in accordance with the provisions of Act 14,346 and the Civil and Commercial Code of the Argentine Nation as regards to the non-abusive exercise of rights on the part of the responsible parties-the licensee of the Zoo of Buenos Aires City and Autonomous City of Buenos Aires." Additionally, the judge required experts from the university and zoo to prepare a binding report specifying what measures the city would adopt in relation to Sandra, including guaranteed improvements in her management to "preserve her cognitive skills."

AFADA was understandably disappointed with the decision to not relocate Sandra promptly, but they were not deterred. Surely, physical conditions would soon be improved for Sandra within her current enclosure. The City of Buenos Aires and their Zoo staff and consultants from the University produced a report that would improve the overall facilities for Sandra as well as activities that would help stimulate her mind. Our expert team also contributed a number of recommendations to the court regarding Sandra's well-being and continued to advocate for her relocation to a sanctuary in either Brazil or Florida.

During the litigation over Sandra's fate, the city was rethinking the future of captive animal management. Buenos Aires mayor, Horacio Rodríguez Larreta, finally had to admit it was time to close the antiquated zoo after one hundred forty years. Additionally, too many animals had died in recent years creating a publicity nightmare. The solution was to rebrand the zoo in 2016 as an ecopark and transfer most of the remaining animals to nature reserves. It was reported in the press (Guardian, 2016) that fifty of the animals, including Sandra, were to stay in the ecopark. This announcement seemed to be a slap in the face to all the efforts to liberate Sandra from the zoo. If the zoo was closing, why keep Sandra there? Part of the answer was that zoo staff truly cared about Sandra and felt that relocating her would be risky for her health. There were, however, those at the zoo and the city of Buenos Aires who did advocate for her transfer to a sanctuary. All along our team advocated for one of two sanctuaries: Great Apes Sanctuary of Sorocaba, Brazil or the Center for Great Apes in Wauchula, Florida, the only accredited sanctuary for orangutans in North America.

AFADA, once again appealed the decision to the Contentious Administrative and Tax Court of Appeals where we assisted the animal legal firm by submitting further recommendations about orangutan cognitive abilities, sensitivity, needs, and the level of suffering they can experience. On June 14, 2016, three judges for the court, Schafrik, Diaz, and Lima, essentially upheld the previous ruling stating that "...she (Sandra) must be protected from ill-treatment and from any kind of cruelty acts, since she is a being with sensitivity." They concluded the City of Buenos Aires "will have to maintain the orangutan's enclosure in conditions adequate to her species; will have to establish animal welfare indicators, of a behavioral complexity and of affective states; will have to explore the possibility of conforming social structures under supervision; and will have to plan daily activities, nourishing and periodical clinical observations, as well as regular and nonintrusive measurements of stress."

Judge Liberatori continued to monitor the progress of Sandra's enclosure and the programs the zoo or ecopark committed to put in place for Sandra. At the same time, plans were made to seek a sanctuary for Sandra outside of Argentina. It seems that while AFADA did not succeed in freeing Sandra in a timely fashion, her care had been improved and her transfer was being planned.

Very little information was being shared about Sandra during late-2017 and 2018. She was living at the "ecopark" in an improved situation under the judge's orders. Then in late April 2019, I had heard from Patti Ragan of the Center for Great Apes (CGA) that the process for bringing Sandra to the United States was underway. The judge and the city had cleared the way. Permits from U.S. Fish and Wildlife and the Centers for Disease Control had been filed. On May 3, 2019, the United States Federal Register listed USFW permit number 08553D by the applicant, Sedgwick County Zoological Society to receive an orangutan from Buenos Aires. The publication allowed the public to comment on this request. Sandra would need to come to the Sedgewick County Zoo for quarantine before being able to travel from Kansas to Florida. Later in the month, I was contacted by the AFADA lawyer who started the legal case, Pablo Buompadre, via Facebook after his recovery from a motorcycle accident that had him in an induced coma for a period. He wanted to talk to me about Sandra's case. My call to him was unanswered except that his girlfriend messaged me saying that Pablo had visited Sandra and saw she wasn't happy. I later learned that Pablo was actually now opposed to the transfer of Sandra to the CGA preferring that she stayed in South America and go to the Brazilian ape sanctuary. Apparently, the talk in the press in Argentina and Brazil of this international transfer of Sandra from Argentina to the zoo and sanctuary in the U.S. was costly and smacked of "big business." Perhaps Latin American pride once again overshadowed the best interests of Sandra and her future, for the facility in Brazil did not have any orangutans to potentially befriend Sandra, only chimpanzees. Regardless, her move to the sanctuary in Florida was already approved and was happening.

On September 27, Sandra who was lightly sedated in a transfer cage was accompanied by ecopark staff on an American Airline Cargo flight from Buenos Aires to the United States. According to American Airlines Cargo, "Sandra arrived safely at Dallas-Fort Worth International Airport (DFW) after an 11-hour flight from Ezeiza International Airport (EZE) in one of the airline's B787-8 aircraft." She was then driven to Kansas and arrived in her quarantine facility "in perfect condition" according to ecopark director, Federico Iglesias. There she spent time receiving medical tests and waiting until the temperature cooled down.

While I was in Indonesia, I received word from Patti that Sandra had been transferred to Florida. Her travel was without fanfare, as Patti wanted. She arrived on November 4, in great condition. While Sandra may have lost her personhood status as an orangutan in the United States, she was greeted by staff as a rock star. Sandra is now getting to know the many residents at the sanctuary on her own terms, based on her choice to interact or not. The last I heard, Sandra had befriended an adult male, Jethro, in a relationship that developed slowly at Sandra's choosing. I am very happy that I had a part in Sandra's story and that the first non-human person will have a long and satisfying life at her sanctuary in Florida.

If the story of Sandra seems complicated as I've relayed it, there was even more I did not discuss. What's significant, pulling information from my earlier chapters, is that a non-human person had been recognized by a court of law for the first time with the right to be represented by legal counsel and advocates concerning her protection. Sandra was recognized as a sentient being, not as a mere thing. The Argentinian legal system has evolved to recognize the tenets of the Declaration on Great Apes, which seeks to extend to non-human great apes the protection of three basic interests: the right to life, the protection of individual liberty, and the prohibition of torture.

Initiated by The Great Ape Project, a book edited by Peter Singer and Paola Cavalieri (1993), and a larger movement, the Declaration on Great Apes situates the great apes (humans, bonobos, chimpanzees, gorillas, and orangutans) within a "community of equals." Yes, if we are to be fair about the matter and make judgments based on genetic evidence, we humans are great apes. Members of the "community of equals" may not be killed (except when in self-defense); they are not to be deprived of their liberty and are entitled to immediate release where there has been no form of due process; and they are not to be tortured, which is defined as the deliberate infliction of extreme pain (with Sandra, the bar was lowered to include suffering). The backers of the Declaration initially sought endorsement by the United Nations with implementation in each country. However, this has proven futile so far. Efforts to get the Declaration on Great Apes or its provisions adopted by individual countries have sometimes moved in parallel with other efforts to promote animal rights or welfare in general. For example, while New Zealand completely banned invasive research on great apes in 1999, the country took a monumental step forward for all animals, allowing them to be legally recognized as "sentient" beings (Bekoff, 2015). An amendment to New Zealand law, on behalf of The Animal Welfare Amendment Bill, May 12, 2015, states that animals, like humans, are "sentient" beings. In 2007, the Balearic Islands (Spain) passed the world's first legislation effectively granting legal personhood rights to all great apes. Spain followed recognizing great ape personhood a year later (Fox, 2012). Religious resistance in Spain eventually kept this effort from being adopted throughout the country. Nevertheless, other countries such as Germany, Austria, the Netherlands, and Sweden have completely banned the use of great apes in animal testing. Switzerland amended its constitution in 1992 to recognize animals as beings and not things (le News, 2016). And in a recent court ruling, Ecuador interpreted the country's "rights of nature" law to give legal rights to individual wild animals rather than personhood status. The ruling was based on a "habeas corpus" case filed by the owner of a captive woolly monkey named Estrellita whose confiscation by authorities led the ruling that not only did the authorities violate Estrellita's rights, but so did the owner under the "rights of nature" argument (Frost, 2022). Wild individual animals now have the right not to be hunted, fished, captured, collected, extracted, kept, retained, trafficked, traded or exchanged. Similar "rights of nature" laws now exist in Colombia, New Zealand, Panama, Chile and Mexico.

The Declaration on Great Apes has created the narrative to push for personhood status for great apes using the same arguments I have been making and by crafting a "community of equals" concept shared by human, chimpanzee, bonobo, gorilla, and orangutan. If Neanderthals still lived among us, we would also welcome them to the "community of equals." Certainly, Homo sapiens outcompeted, exterminated, and/or genetically absorbed collateral hominin leaving the great apes as our closest living primate relatives. We have historically seen ourselves as superior to other species which we have treated as things for our own use. Only a few countries have thus far granted personhood status to great apes (Balearic Islands and Argentina), though I can only hope more will be added to this list by the time you read these words.

Nevertheless, great apes are, at the very least, afforded improved animal welfare laws protecting them from the torture of invasive experimentation. It may be easier for more liberal cultures to adopt the position of ending torture and suffering to animals before giving great apes rights as non-human persons.

Interestingly, many countries in Africa, a continent where human rights are frequently abused and where bush meat might include dried chimpanzee or gorilla flesh, have signed onto the Kinshasa Declaration on Great Apes (UNEP, 2005). The Kinshasa Declaration was crafted under the auspices of the United Nation's Great Ape Survival Program (GRASP) following a September 2005 meeting of the first GRASP range and donor country members. This was a document focused on the conservation of wild great apes. Nowhere in the declaration was there any mention of the sentient or sapient qualities of great apes. More than seventy representatives including eighteen range states, six donor countries, twenty-five non-governmental organization partners, two Multilateral Environmental Agreement partnerships, and two intergovernmental organizations signed the document affirming a commitment to protect great apes.

The role of great apes in the conservation arena is less controversial than their presence in the "community of equals." At the same time, protecting them in the wild has been as challenging to accomplish, as getting governments to open their eyes, minds, and hearts to recognize great apes as sentient beings. Since Kinshasa, the status of great apes throughout their range has gone from bad to worse (Stiles, 2023), despite the many laws each country adopts to protect great apes on paper. Seventy to eighty percent of wild great apes live outside of national parks and protected areas (Strindberg, 2018). While they perform eco-engineering services to maintain the health and vitality of forest ecosystems, they remain vulnerable to the same forces that have driven their numbers to critically endangered levels, which is the case for all orangutan species and subspecies. Conferences, declarations, and action plans will not change the trajectory of these species' decline. Only when those humans who are in conflict with the great apes come to see them as ecologically important and sentient beings rather than pests or game to be eaten will the great apes have a real chance for survival in the wild. Engendering "compassionate conservation" (Bekoff, et al., 2020) would also go far to further this transformation of attitude. This will take intense and prolonged education initiatives as much as enforcing the laws that protect all species. This is something that I have spoken about over the years and try to integrate into the outreach and conservation programs we do in the field where human-wildlife conflict exists.

Orangutan Ethics and Choice

In the 1996 paper, "Orangutan Ethics," Biruté Galdikas and I argue that orangutans have personhood status and deserve basic rights. Besides their genetic, evolutionary, and biological similarities to humans, we provided examples in natural and experimental settings where orangutans demonstrate their advanced cognitive skills and their theory of mind to deceive or manipulate others. We mentioned how sensitive orangutans are and recounted the story of the orangutan Jimmy, though not by name, who, you'll recall, died of a broken heart. Orangutan sentience, intellect, and awareness were on display at Camp Leakey every day, making it clear that the differences between our two species were only a matter of degree, not of kind.

At Camp Leakey, we respected the individual personhood of each orangutan. We always insisted that 1. Humans are only the first among equals and that 2. Orangutans have the same rights as humans within their own orangutan environment, which is the forest, while 3. Humans have rights within their own camp environment, which are the buildings. Orangutans at Camp Leakey, therefore, had the choice of returning to the nearby forest on their own or being bi-cultural residents of the camp. This matter of choice was very important in the rehabilitation philosophy at Camp Leakey whereby orangutans were free to come and go on their own. Galdikas practiced a form of guided "choice" in the rehabilitation process. While each orangutan's physical and medical well-being was addressed in a timely fashion, his or her emotional well-being was given the time needed to make the psychological adjustments in transitioning to the wild. If orangutans were "sober" citizens of Camp Leakey, they had the right to choose the time of their return to the forest. Some orangutans, such as the adolescents or adults we were required to accept from Javanese zoos, quickly left Camp Leakey for the nearby forests on their own, never to be seen again. Others remained bi-cultural. These are mainly females who, by their very nature, stay in the area of their birth while males tend to emigrate out to eventually claim their own territory. When fruit is plentiful in the nearby forest, females may spend many days or weeks away from Camp Leakey. Food scarcity in their home range may goad many to come to the feeding station, especially if they are nursing their children. They are not forced to be at the feeding station, but having this nutritional safety net was the humane thing to do for individuals whose early years were shattered by less-than-humane poachers. Nowadays, the orangutans' presence at the feeding station enables local tour operators to earn an income by bringing local and international visitors to witness orangutan personalities and behavior first-hand.

The more modern approach in rescue and reintroduction is to transfer orangutans to increasingly remote forests that are protected and barred to visitors. If the orangutans are ex-captive, they are to be reintroduced to a forested area that does not have a viable population of wild orangutans to avoid contamination of disease or unnatural culture. While the animals are initially monitored and assessed as to their survival skills, the choice is made by the human to relocate one or more individuals to a forested area. No one asks the orangutans if this is what they want. It is not uncommon to return an orangutan to a care center after the individual fails to thrive as a free-ranging, reintroduced orangutan.

The Camp Leakey orangutan situation of the 1970s and early 1980s was such that orangutans chose to come and go as they pleased. For those orangutans who repeatedly abused their rights by routinely breaking into buildings and stealing or destroying valuable items inside, there were consequences. It was our choice to dispense justice and in the harshest cases, banish the perpetrator to a more rapid reintroduction than he or she perhaps wanted. Such was the case with Sugito, Galdikas's beloved, adopted orangutan son (Galdikas, 1995), whom she raised shortly after she came to Camp Leakey in 1971. He was the reason for my being invited to Camp Leakey in the first place. As mentioned earlier, Sugito was the juvenile suspected of killing another orangutan, but he didn't want any part of me or my sign teaching lessons. Nevertheless, he did like to break into buildings and steal food or other items of perceived value. Rod Brindamour, Galdikas's husband at the time, had grown to hate Sugito for a variety of reasons, not least of which was Sugito's disdain for Brindamour. As I recounted previously, Sugito would express his displeasure in many different ways including biting Brindamour or peeing on him in bed (Thompson, 2010). Sugito knew of Brindamour's passion for repairing the camp generator, so Sugito would frequently break into the machine shed, pull all the important cables, and disconnect the fuel line from the generator and diesel engine.

Sugito lost all rights and privilege to life at Camp Leakey after breaking into Brindamour's home and ransacking it totally on September 7, 1978. He and his other orangutan "partners in crime" spilled chemicals from the small lab cabinet and broke equipment. When I explained this to Brindamour upon his return to Camp Leakey two days later, he decided it was time to relocate Sugito to another portion of the Tanjung Puting Reserve. But that didn't actually happen until Sugito committed his last act of larceny by breaking into the student quarters and stealing money and important papers. On September 22, 1978, Sugito was anesthetized and taken by boat to Natai Lengkuas, an area many miles from Camp Leakey where he became an independent, free-ranging orangutan. With rights and choices come responsibilities and consequences.

Choice for orangutans within the experimental setting has been discussed previously. Rinnie was given the choice to participate in the signing sessions. She did not have to sit down and work with me, and on some days she didn't. Captive great apes may have the choice not to participate in non-invasive experimental sessions but engage many times out of boredom. Most institutionalized orangutans, like Sandra, do not have much choice in their lives. Rinnie, at the end of the study, had the choice to return to the wild and be a free-ranging orangutan without human interference. Great ape and especially orangutan choice in research studies has been examined by academics but note how my field experience is lived knowledge in a natural setting.

Choice was given to Princess when I returned to Camp Leakey in 1981 to test a hypothesis for my dissertation. After a year away from her, she forgot many of the signs she previously learned. I started by measuring the effort needed to re-teach her ten signs to a criterion of performance. In a separate test, her relative interest in the referents of the signs was ascertained by allowing her to manually choose one of two items placed before her. For example, I placed a peanut next to a piece of candy or a hat next to a pair of glasses. All possible pairwise combinations of the referents were presented twice in order to balance out bias for the left or right placement. After I placed the items on a table or seat of a chair, I asked her to pick one. She was not rewarded with food after making the choice. After calculating the added scores for all pairwise combinations of items, a list of items of ranking interest was developed. Not surprisingly, food items topped the list. These are also the signs that are learned fastest. Of course, some signs with difficult manual movements were harder to learn than signs with simple hand gestures. However, when I compared the sign learning and the referent interest measures, I found the correlation was significant indicating she learned signs more quickly when the referent of the sign was an item of greater interest (Shapiro, 1985). The use of choice was a way to determine relative interest by an orangutan in a non-invasive manner. It would be possible, in my opinion, to use pairwise presentations of images and other items to have orangutans, like Sandra, express their interest and possible choice in various opportunities presented to them.

Having a choice in selecting what to do for an individual who is incarcerated provides an illusion of the freedom of choice. Just as jailed humans will have their choices taken away or given back as a form of punishment or reward, the illusion of freedom becomes a reward in itself. For the individual who has been spoiled as a youngster, given abundant choices in pleasures and material resources growing up, then abruptly having those choices removed or limited can be seen as punishment causing suffering to the individual. Imagine what anguish was experienced by the orangutan Chantek when he was taken from his amazing upbringing with mobility and privilege as a signing ape and then, through no fault of his own, relocated to a cage. His mobility and choices were now substantially limited. For an orangutan like Sandra who was brought up in a more impoverished environment, being able to have even a small choice in affecting her environment would give her a sense of control and would be rewarding. In psychology, the positive and negative contrast effect (Crespi, 1942) illustrates the relative strength of how even small rewards can have large impacts on behavior.

The discussion section of the paper Galdikas and I wrote (1996) serves as a logical ending to this section about rights for orangutans. In it, we make the case that apart from the ecological reasons for conserving orangutans, there is a reason for orangutans themselves in as much as they share so much of our genetic code, a "smoking gun" of our biological closeness and a common ancestor millions of years ago (today we believe 16-20mya). For us, the rights for orangutans as described in the Declaration on Great Apes (life, freedom, no torture) logically follow since such rights are surely derived from their closeness to the species, humans, which seemingly holds dominion over the planet. This would be consistent with recognizing rights among all within the "community of equals": humans, chimpanzees, bonobos, gorillas and orangutans. Orangutans, like the African apes, are our pongid cousins. It is worth repeating that orangutans show advanced and comparable cognitive skills as the other great apes, exhibit "Machiavellian" social intelligence, develop sensory-motor intelligence in parallel fashion as human children for the first two years (Chevalier-Skolnikoff, et al., 1982), and learn to communicate with sign language. Their emotions and personalities are recognizable by humans as not that different from our own. I've marshalled plenty of significant evidence throughout this book for this claim, but notably, I have first-hand experience with orangutans in various stages of the wild and in their development to make these assertions.

So while I suggest that orangutans deserve certain rights, as do all great apes, the most important right for the orangutans is the right to live undisturbed within their natural rainforest habitat on Borneo and Sumatra. Should it be a matter of "simian sovereignty", which Goodin, et al. (1997) consider as a mechanism for territorial protection? In their paper, they examine the epistemological and historical perspective on the concepts of sovereignty, concluding with ways in which such sovereignty mechanisms could be employed for great apes. Sovereignty has both assertive and defensive meanings: "controlling influence" and "freedom from external control: autonomy" (Merriam-Webster, 2019). If sovereignty status for orangutans in their native habitat is recognized, how would it be implemented? The most logical mechanism would allow human advocates to represent the orangutans and to act as guardians on their behalf, much like in cases of personhood status.

Unfortunately, obtaining internationally recognized sovereignty would not automatically solve the problem for orangutans as territorially protected "people of the forest." All levels of society, particularly those at the wildlife interface level, would need to respect such status and not violate the integrity of the sovereignty agreement. That will be challenging, if the historical efficacy of the current laws is any guide, but it could provide the legal basis to take action in court against those who would not respect the boundaries of the sovereign territory and engage in unauthorized activities (e.g., agriculture, mining, hydroelectric projects).

While I have been making the case for orangutan personhood and rights based on just how much alike we are, the argument for giving them some form of territorial sovereignty might be bolstered by considering the services they perform for maintaining the integrity and health of the forest. As I've emphasized, differences count. That is, great apes, especially orangutans, exhibit a sustainable land ethic unlike the economic-centered ethic of humans. Like eco-engineers, orangutans keep a low profile, but we know they perform seed dispersal, fertilization of the forest floor with their droppings, and enhancing sunlight to the forest floor by clearing out the deadwood from the canopy. Through these activities, seedlings take root, saplings race to the sky, and trees sequester carbon as they photosynthesize and grow. Orangutans work like eco-engineers as they struggle to survive in their forest environment (Tague, 2020). We all benefit from their presence since they facilitate the maintenance of forests, which reduce carbon dioxide in the atmosphere while providing oxygen, rainfall, and many other ecological services. In fact, economists have recently quantified in human currency how much the everyday activities of large wild mammals such as elephants and whales are worth compared to alternative investments in the environment, and the results demonstrate just how important they are (Chami, et al., 2020). While economists have yet to run the calculations for orangutans, I suspect that we would be surprised at how much value they provide us over the course of their lifetime. Can moral and pragmatic factors sway Indonesian leaders to grant orangutans territorial sovereignty for survival? Some of us are not waiting to find out. Many orangutan advocacy groups along with other medium and large NGOs are negotiating with the Indonesian government to co-manage protected areas like national parks or protection forests under a Memorandum of Understanding (MoU), or to control and manage former logging concessions as a sustainable business. Since most orangutans live outside of national parks, finding large, state-owned forests landscapes of the right size, shape and topography that have orangutan populations or that could support released ex-captive orangutans is a priority.

Many of us are turning towards the forest concession approach including a license to allow an Indonesian business entity to help restore and/or maintain the ecological integrity of the forest landscape in its natural state. Obtaining a private forest concession is a long application process requiring surveys, fees, and government approval, but the business that receives the license has the right and control over activities within the parcel. Over the length of the forest concession period, some forty years, the business must pay concession fees to the government. These are costs that would have been paid by a logging, palm oil, or mining company competing for the same landscape to manage according to their business plan.

Those handling the Forest Concession during its term of operation will essentially have sovereignty over the concession. That means the orangutans living within the forest concession will be effectively protected by both the national laws as well as the rights afforded to a corporation operating the forest concession business. Sitting the forest concessions adjacent to already protected forests is an advantageous way to increases the overall landscape size for a species that can wander for many kilometers. It is part of the challenging process of acquiring the government approved licenses for available and practical parcels of forest land that have significant conservation value. It is difficult competing for available forest land that other companies are also seeking, especially when multiple approvals by local, regional, and national government officials are required. There is no guarantee that months and years of work will bear fruit, particularly when the lengthy and complex system of approving a license can fail the applicant for a number of reasons. Another challenge of operating a forest concession, or any type of concession management plan, is working cooperatively with the local community.

In some cases, there have been ownership disputes with members of the local community over traditional lands taken by the national government and gazetted as state land during the Soeharto era. Many have petitioned to have their lands returned to customary or "adat" status which would benefit families and villages in the area. Understanding the local situation before beginning the application process is therefore important. Since creating a plan to generate revenue is part of what has to happen in the application to the government, involving the locals within the business model can help reduce conflicts and provide a future livelihood for them.

In our paper, Galdikas and I (1996) conclude that without a massive commitment to human economic rights, orangutan rights will suffer. Developing equitable strategies for orangutan survival will require working with local people and habitat governments in a cooperative fashion. Without an emphasis on both human economic rights and orangutan rights, both the moral and practical advantages of people's concerns with orangutan ethics will vanish.

A Call to Action

The Dayak groups of Borneo have traditionally considered orangutans another tribe of people. Without the western bias of Cartesian thinking, many of the Dayak and other indigenous peoples around the world have recognized the importance of nonhuman animals and nature within their lives and belief systems. While a portion of people in the West have acknowledged and benefited from this deep and long-known understanding of living in harmony with nature, perhaps we, as a whole, would take the existential threat of global climate change more seriously if we all thought as much with our hearts as with our heads.

But what does this mean? I think it is important to recognize that saving orangutans also means saving other biodiversity that share the orangutan's habitat, the rainforests of Kalimantan and Sumatra. And if we accept this, then we can also infer that by saving orangutans we are also saving ourselves, as large tracts of healthy biodiverse rainforests rely on such large seed-dispersing animals. Most naturally, having healthy rainforests will have a positive effect on climate change. They are, after oceans, one of the important lungs of the planet after all.

So, what you can do, easily and meaningfully, today?

1) Donate. Donate to experienced organizations that directly collaborate with local people who benefit directly

from the success of the projects. Also support groups that work with other government and non-government organizations on larger projects. They generally share the results of projects with their peers.

It is amazing to consider that small but regular donations to an effective organization can empower it when multiplied by thousands of similar such donations - affordable when recognizing a monthly donation of $10 is the price of drinking three Skinny Vanilla Lattes from Starbucks. Would saving orangutans be worth giving up three drinks? That is a choice we can make.

2) Volunteer. Another way to support orangutans and related biodiversity is by volunteering your time and skills to help at a reputable and related nonprofit. Smaller organizations rely on the passion and commitment of individuals who can engage in various functions, projects, and programs to fulfill the group's mission.

OURF has been fortunate to have had the support of many volunteers over the years. I wish to thank those who have joined our organization since its inception as well as many who joined me during my early days at OFI. Not only has their thought leadership and sweat equity been appreciated, but so has their friendship and commitment to the cause.

It has been shown that volunteering is a choice we can make that provides multiple benefits to our health and well-being. It has been implicated in adding years to our lives as participating in philanthropic activities provides a sense of meaning and purpose. We need that more than ever as an antidote in a world where the daily news bombards our psyche with doom and gloom. As Gandhi said, "The best way to find yourself is to lose yourself in the service of others."

3) Shop Smartly. The power of the pocketbook in the global retail world is immense as corporate shareholders are sensitive to the purchasing decisions of consumers. Behind each plastic-wrapped, eye-catching package, there is a backstory. Read labels and choose products that do the least harm to the environment and society. Let's take, for example, a commodity that is in nearly half of the products on typical grocery store shelves today: palm oil.

I would be shocked if anyone reading this book hasn't heard stories about how the palm oil industry has impacted orangutans and their rainforest habitat. Vast tracts of biodiverse forests have been decimated and transformed into estate monoculture plantations of oil palm (*Elaeis guineensis*) to produce this most productive and versatile oil. Hundreds of thousands of orangutans have perished over the course of many decades, first in Sumatra and more recently in Borneo, where desperate orangutans have been killed as pests wandering into or through large plantations. Does this mean we should boycott palm oil? I don't think so. While the commodity has been vilified, people should realize that the problem is not palm oil, but how big business has taken a cash crop and turned it into a global industry without factoring in the environmental and social costs and casualties.

Since 2004, efforts have been made to tame the palm oil industry by enforcing and auditing sustainable palm oil production. The Roundtable on Sustainable Palm Oil (RSPO) has become the gold standard in creating a transparent system of accountability with the goal of moving the industry towards certified sustainability. That means for growers, not exploiters. While not perfect, the RSPO continues to strengthen the principles and criteria of certified "sustainable" palm oil. So, when the product you are shopping for has palm oil in it, check for the RSPO logo featuring an oil palm leaf as its stamp of approval. While there have been complaints about the efficacy of the RSPO to hold certain members accountable for not abiding by the standards in the real world, the RSPO does have a complaints process that operates in a bureaucratic fashion which takes time.

To help expedite your search for sustainable products, there are downloadable apps for your smartphone that can be used to provide guidance. Some app developers not only have done their homework on the ingredients, but they are also tracking the movement of the companies heading in the right direction. See the resource section of this book for more information.

4) Visit orangutan viewing areas. By visiting orangutan viewing areas, you will show the local government officials that rainforests and wildlife are, in fact, sustainable sources of local income. Tourism is a multi-billion dollar industry that caters to a wide range of travelers from those who like to cruise to others who will rent an Airbnb home or room. Wealthy individuals will pay premium prices to stay at exclusive locations, seeking a pampered experience. One of the niche industries within tourism is ecotourism. As the name implies, ecotourism seeks to bring the tourist closer to nature in a way that encourages environmentally friendly practices, protects the natural and cultural heritage of a destination, and supports local communities. Ecotourism goes by many names such as sustainable tourism, green tourism, nature tourism, responsible tourism, ethical tourism, mindful travel, conscious travel, and pro-poor tourism. One of the principles is education and learning more about the people and local environment. Typically, ecotour groups are smaller than traditional tour groups and seek to leave footprints and take only photos.

Before the Covid pandemic shut down ecotourism to orangutan viewing areas, thousands of people from around the world would come to Pangkalan Bun in Central Kalimantan each year on their own or with the assistance of a tour operator to purchase their park permits, rent a boat, and make their way up the Sekonyer River. The pandemic put hundreds of local people out of work including tour guides and their assistants, boat owners, boat operators, and assistants as well as ecolodge staff and management.

Now, National Parks, including Tanjung Puting, have opened up and ecotourism is returning. Most of the orangutan viewing areas can be visited, but I would advise checking the current situation at the destinations you are considering. Numerous local and regional ecotour operators that are available can offer complete or partial packages including park permits, food, transportation, and lodging (at ecolodges or preferably on the kelotoks). The kelotoks are now becoming increasingly more comfortable some even with air-conditioned cabins.

5) Avoid Performing Orangutan Shows. Observing orangutans can be a fascinating experience, but it is important to address the ethical problem of orangutans in street performances, circuses, and their interactions with tourists. Travelers to Asia may encounter orangutans in various parks and entertainment establishments. However, the use of orangutans for entertainment raises serious ethical concerns. In Thailand, boxing orangutans have been in the news and are condemned by many in the West, but tourism still thrives in these businesses.

Performing orangutans are trained to perform unnatural behaviors that are contrary to their natural behavior in the wild. They are often subjected to long hours of training which can include physical punishment, deprivation of food, water, and social contact, leading to physical and psychological problems. Additionally, young orangutans who interact with tourists often come from the illegal pet trade and are exposed to diseases from the public.

To address the issue of unethical orangutan performances, individuals can take several actions. First, they can avoid supporting businesses that use orangutans for entertainment. Consumers can choose to boycott circuses and other forms of entertainment that use live orangutans to send a message that there is no demand for this type of exploitation. Second, individuals can help raise awareness about the unethical treatment of orangutans by talking to friends and family, sharing information on social media, and supporting organizations that advocate for their welfare. Third, motivated people can contact their elected representatives to express their concerns about the use of orangutans for entertainment and advocate for stronger laws to protect these animals. Finally, individuals who witness abuse or mistreatment of orangutans in entertainment can report it to animal welfare organizations or local authorities.

6) Leave a message for government and corporate decisionmakers. You probably already have some opinions about many of the topics I have covered, from the ethical aspects of how orangutans are treated to the larger environmental challenges we face collectively, including rainforest degradation and destruction. Let elected government officials and business leaders know how you feel and what you would like to see happen to improve the situation. You can do this in a way that is both from the heart and effective. While emails are now commonplace ways to quickly communicate to elected officials, a well-written personal letter may be the best way to communicate with them. Elected officials are interested in knowing how their constituents feel about issues, especially when those issues involve decisions made by them. They know that for every letter they receive on

an issue, many more people also feel that way but didn't take the time to send a letter.

Writing a letter expressing your heartfelt concerns does a number of things. First, the elected official may not know about the specific issue you are writing about so you can inform them about the background and history about the topic. Second, building a thoughtful constituent reputation enhances your influence, making your opinions and support more impactful. Third, if your voice is one of many on the same topic, the elected official will look deeper into the issue as the official knows that they are being watched by others.

Just be sure to stay informed about legislation at local, state, and national levels that could benefit orangutans, biodiversity, and rainforests. While officials outside Indonesia may not directly influence orangutan-related laws, they could impact rainforests and biodiversity within their own jurisdictions. For instance, consider the ongoing efforts in California to pass the California Deforestation-free Procurement Act, which aims to prevent companies with state contracts from contributing to tropical deforestation and violations of indigenous rights. With California being the world's fifth-largest economy and a significant purchaser of forest-risk commodities, this legislation holds substantial potential. As constituents, Californians can advocate for the passage of laws that safeguard orangutans, biodiversity, forests, and climate, considering California's ambitious goals to reduce greenhouse gas emissions and end deforestation by 2030.

The same concept holds true for corporations. Let them know with your email and your wallets, but you must do both, or the change you want to see will not happen.

7) Educate others. You can make a difference. Never let it be said that one person cannot make a difference. Teenager Greta Thunberg went from being a lonely, solitary figure who sat and demonstrated in front of the Swedish parliament to being an outspoken icon of youth activism for the environment within a couple of years.

For our beleaguered orangutan cousins, how many human beings could potentially speak out? If we use a population estimate of 115,000 Bornean, Sumatran and Tapanuli orangutans and 8 billion humans, each orangutan theoretically has over 69,000 potential human advocates. Of course, the number also means there are over 69,000 times more humans than orangutans competing for the planet's available resources. Orangutans don't ask for much, certainly not for smartphones, washing machines, and fast cars. They only want freedom and forest to live out their lives. As someone who has not been afraid of calling Princess, the orangutan, his adopted daughter, I feel as if there are potentially more than enough humans on this planet who have the heart and fortitude to speak out and educate others on behalf of their distant primate cousin. I invite you to be one of them.

Still, education is just the beginning of the journey toward saving the orangutans. As you have read this book, you have already taken a significant step toward making a difference. But the journey doesn't end here: you must recognize the impact we have on the world around us and take responsibility for your actions. In the words of Dr. Jane Goodall, "You cannot get through a single day without having an impact on the world around you. What you do makes a difference, and you have to decide what kind of difference you want to make."

We must remain vigilant and remain undistracted by a multitude of stimuli vying for our attention, and remain focused and determined in our mission to help save orangutans suffering in captivity and endangered in the wild.

We can take action to support the preservation of biodiversity of Planet Earth, and help ensure a time will soon come when all orangutans are finally out of the cage.

Additional Resources

To learn more about the work of the Orang Utan Republik Foundation and what you can do to take action, visit www.orangutanrepublik.org

The full resolution, color Galleries may be found here: https://drive.google.com/drive/folders/1-EYHL_Oz-3KzAk2sgo9cTmQI8Ue9zdRQF

To learn more about the impressive work of our partners, The Orangutan Project, visit their website at: www.theorangutanproject.org

Please visit the Orang Utan Republik Foundation's Social Media Channels:

Facebook:
https://www.facebook.com/OrangUtanRepublik

Twitter:
https://www.twitter.com/OURF

Instagram:
https://www.instagram.com/orangutanrepublik/

YouTube:
https://www.youtube.com/orangutanrepublik

Sustainable Palm Oil Resources from the Cheyenne Mountain Zoo:
https://www.cmzoo.org/conservation/orangutans-palm-oil/

Gallery Credits

Unless otherwise noted by the name of the photographer or contributor, the images are from my personal collection comprising a curated selection in three galleries blending my captures and contributions graciously provided by individuals some of whose names elude my memory.
I do know that the following individuals had taken photographs provided to me over the years though I am not necessarily certain which images they took including: Richard Haas, Robert Summers, Allen Altchech, Inggriani Shapiro, Birute Galdikas, Dianne Taylor-Snow, Michelle Desilets, Harvey Jordan, Leonora Wiryo, official palace photographer, official conference photographer.

I extend my heartfelt gratitude to all of them for the privilege of showcasing these visual treasures within the pages of this book.

Gallery One

1: Rod Brindamour
2 - 17: Personal Collection
18: Rod Brindamour

Gallery Two

1 - 4: Personal Collection
5: Rod Brindamour
6: Personal Collection
7 - 12: Rod Brindamour
13 - 32: Personal Collection
33 - 35: Rod Brindamour
36 - 50: Personal Collectionn

Gallery Three

1 - 6: Personal Collection

7: Personal Collection. (Featuring Lillian Rachlin, Jeanette Tonnies, Blanche Whittey, Filomena Galdikas, and David Churchman)

8 - 9: Personal Collection
10 - 12: Marcus Phipps
13: Maurine Taubman
14 - 15: Personal Collection
16: Wendy Hoole-Cundiff
17 - 28: Personal Collection
29 - 30: Roberto Angel Garcia
31: Center for Great Apes
32 - 33: Personal Collection

34: Peter Ney. (Featuring Susan Callery, Ed Begley Jr., TV Producer David Helfant, Singer/Actress Katey Sagal, Leif Cocks, and Tom Eddington.)

35: Stanley Bratawira. (Featuring singer Malea Emma, Ed Begley Jr., Pongo recipient Dianna Cohen, "Kid Conservationist" Jack Dalton, and former Pongo recipients Topher White and Ronna Phelps)

36: Personal Collection

Bibliography

Bekoff, Marc. 2015. "New Zealand Declares Animals to be Sentient, Bans Testing."*Psychology Today*. https://www.psychologytoday.com/ca/blog/animal-emotions201506/new-zealand-declares-animals-be-sentient-bans-testing

Brosnan, Sarah F., Hillary C. Schiff and Frans B. M. de Waal. 2004. "Tolerance for Inequity May Increase with Social Closeness in Chimpanzees." *Proceedings of the Royal Society. B* doi:10.1098/rspb.2004.2947.

Brosnan Sarah, et al. 2011. "Orangutans (*Pongo pygmaeus*) Do Not Form Expectations Based on Their Partner's Outcomes." *Folia Primatol* 2011. 82. 56-70.

Brown, Jerram L. 1975. *The Evolution of Behavior*. NY: Norton.

Cajal, Santiago Ramon y. 1995. *Histology of the nervous system of man and vertebrates, Volume 1*. Oxford: Oxford UP.

Carne, Charlotte, et al., 2014. "The Risk of Disease to Great Apes: Simulating Disease Spread in Orangutan (*Pongo pygmaeus wurmbii*) and Chimpanzee (*Pan troglodytes schweinfurthii*) Association Networks." *Plos One*. 9.4. e95039. doi: 10.1371/journal.pone.0095039

Ceballos, Gerardo, Paul Ehrlich, & PH Raven. 2020. Vertebrates on the brink as indicators of biological annihilation and the sixth mass extinction. Proceedings of the National Academy of Sciences of the United States of America 117, 13596–13602.

Chami, Ralph, Connel Fullenkamp, Fabio Berzaghi, Sonia Español-Jiménez, Milton Marcondes, and Jose Palazzo. 2020. "On Valuing Nature-Based Solutions to Climate Change: A Framework with Application to Elephants and Whales." *Economic Research Initiatives at Duke (ERID) Working Paper No. 297*. Available at SSRN: https://ssrn.com/abstract=3686168 or http://dx.doi.org/10.2139/ssrn.3686168

Chevalier-Skolnikoff, Susan, Birute Galdikas, and Alan Skolnikoff. 1982. "The Adaptive Significance of High Intelligence in Wild Orangutans: A Preliminary Report." *Journal of Human Evolution* 11. 639-652.

Cocks, Leif. 2016. *Orangutans: My Cousins, My Friends.* South Perth, Australia: The Orangutan Project.

Cocks, Leif. 2019. *Finding Our Humanity.* South Perth, Australia: The Orangutan Project.

Crespi, Leo P. 1942. "Quantitative variation of incentive and performance in the white rat." *American Journal of Psychology*, 55, 467-517

Damerius, Laura, et al. 2017. "Orientation Toward Humans Predict Cognitive Performance in Orang-utans". *Scientific Reports* 7. 40052. doi: 10.1038/srep40052.

De Vos, J. M., Joppa, L. N., Gittleman, J. L., Stephens, P. R., & Pimm, S. L. 2015. Estimating the normal background rate of species extinction. Conservation Biology, 29(2), 452-462. https://doi.org/10.1111/cobi.12380

EIA and Telepak Indonesia. 1999. The Final Cut. Illegal Logging in Indonesia's Orangutan Parks. www.eia-international.org.

Fouts, Roger S. 1972. "The Use of Guidance in Teaching Sign Language to a Chimpanzee." *Journal of Comparative and Physiological Psychology* 80. 515-522.

Fouts, Roger S. 1973. "Acquisition and the Testing of Gestural Signs in Four Young Chimpanzees." *Science* 180. 978-980.

Fox, Justin. 2012. "Great Ape Personhood." *Law School Student Scholarship* 102. https://scholarship.shu.edu/student_scholarship/102

Frost, Rosie. 2022. "Wild animals in Ecuador now have legal rights, thanks to a monkey named Estrellita." Euronews.green. https://www.euronews.com/green/2022/04/01/wild-animals-in-ecuador-now-have-legal-rights-thanks-to-a-monkey-named-estrellita

Galdikas, Biruté. 1978. *Orangutan Adaptation at Tanjung Puting Reserve, Central Borneo.* Ann Arbor: University Microfilms Intl.

Galdikas, Biruté, Gary Shapiro, and Flora Katz. 1985. "Danau Burung, a Bird Lake in Southern Indonesian Borneo." Ardea 73. 189-190.

Galdikas, Biruté M.F. 1995. *Reflections of Eden: My Years with the Orangutans of Borneo.* Boston: Little Brown.

Galdikas, Biruté. 1995a. "Social and Reproductive Behavior of Wild Adolescent Female Orangutans." *The Neglected Ape.* Ronald D. Naler, et al., eds. NY: Plenum. 163-182.

Galdikas, Birute and Gary Shapiro. 1994. *A Guidebook to Tanjung Puting National Park*. Jakarta: PT Gramedia Pustaka Utama and the Orangutan Foundation International.

Galdikas, Biruté and Gary Shapiro. 1996. "Orangutan Ethics." *Etica & Animali* 8. 50-67.

Gallup, Gordon G., Jr. 1970. "Chimpanzees: self-recognition." *Science* 167. 86-87.

Gardner, R. Allen and Beatrix Gardner. 1969. "Teaching Sign Language to a Chimpanzee." *Science* 165. 664-672.

Geschwind, Norman. 1970. "Specializations of the Human Brain." *Scientific American* 241 (3). 180-201.

Goodall, Jane. 1971. *In the Shadow of Man*. Boston: Mariner.

Goodin, Robert E., et al. 1997. "Simian Sovereignty." *Political Theory* 25.6. 821-849.

Griggs, David, et al. 2013. "Sustainable Development Goals for People and Planet." *Nature* 495. 305-307.

Harlow, Harry. 1958. "The Nature of Love." *American Psychologist* 13. 573-685.

Harlow, Harry F., et al. 1965. "Total Social Isolation in Monkeys." *PNAS* 54. 90-97.

Hayes, Keith. and Catherine Hayes. 1952. "Imitation in a Home-raised chimpanzee". *Journal of Comparative and Physiological Psychology* 45. 450-459.

Hewes, Gordon W. 1973. "Primate Communication and the Gestural Origins of Language." *Current Anthropology* 14. 5-24.

Hopkins, William. 2006. "Comparative and Familial Analysis of Handedness in Great Apes." *Psychological Bulletin* 132(4). 538–559.

Inggersol, R and Antonina Scarnà. 2023. *Primatology, Ethics and Trauma- The Oklahoma Chimpanzee Studies*. Routledge.

IPPL. 1990. "Smuggled Orangutans Reach Bangkok." *IPPL Newsletter* 17.1. 4-6.

IPPL. 1991. "Update on the Taiwan Ten." *IPPL Newsletter* 18.3. 6.

IUCN, 2022, Redlist, https://www.iucnredlist.org/search?taxonomies=124552&searchType=species

Kellogg, W. N. and L.A. Kellogg. 1933. *The Ape and The Child: A Comparative Study of the Environmental Influence Upon Early Behavior*. New York and London: Hafner Publishing Co.

Leopold, Aldo. 1949. *A Sand County Almanac*. Oxford: OUP.

le News. 2016. "Swiss fact: Switzerland first country to consider dignity of animals in constitution." https://lenews.ch/2016/10/05/swiss-facts-animal-dignity/

Lethmate, Jurgens and Gerti Ducker. 1973."Experiments on Self-Recognition in a Mirror in Orangutans, Chimpanzees, Gibbons and Several Monkey Species." *Zeitschrift für Tierpsychologie*, 33 (3-4). 248-269.

Liberatori, Elena. 2015. "Asociacion de Functionarios y Abogados por los Derechos de los Animales y Otros Contra GCBA Sobre Amparo." https://www.animallaw.info/case/asociacion-de-funcionarios-y-abogados-por-los-derechos-de-los-animales-y-otros-contra-gcba

Linden, Eugene. 1974. *Apes, Men and Language*. Saturday Review Press, pp 304.

Lonsdorf, Elizabeth and William Hopkins. 2005. "Wild chimpanzees show population-level handedness for tool use." *PNAS* 102 (35). 12634 –12638

Lorenz, Konrad. 1965. *Evolution and Modification of Behavior*. Chicago: U Chicago P.

Macfie, Elizabeth and Elizabeth Williamson. 2010. *Best Practice Guidelines for Great Ape Tourism*. Gland, Switzerland: IUCN/SSC Primate Specialty Group.

MacKinnon, John, et al. 1983, Tanjung Puting National Park Management Plan for Development. WWF Report for PHPA, Bogor.

Maggioncalda, Anne, Robert Sapolsky and Nancy Czekala. 1999. "Reproductive Hormone Profiles in Captive Male Orangutans: Implications for Understanding Developmental Arrest." *American Journal of Physical Anthropology*. 109.1. 19-32.

McNeely, Jeffrey and Paul Spencer Wachtel. 1988. *Soul of the Tiger*. NY: Doubleday.

Merriam-Webster. 2019. https://www.merriam-webster.com/

Miles, H. Lyn White. 1993. "Language and the Orangutan: The Old 'Person' of the Forest." *The Great Ape Project: Equality Beyond Humanity*. Paola Cavalieri and Peter Singer, eds. NY: St. Martin's. 42-57.

Miles, H. Lyn White. 1994. "ME CHANTEK: The Development of Self-awareness in a Signing Orangutan." *Self-awareness in Animals and Humans: Developmental Perspectives*. Sue Taylor Parker, Robert W. Mitchell, and Maria L. Boccia, eds. Cambridge: CUP. 254-272.

Mitchell, Robert W. 1993. "Humans, Nonhumans and Personhood." *The Great Ape Project: Equality Beyond Humanity*. Paola Cavalieri and Peter Singer, eds. NY: St. Martin's. 237-247.

Mitchell, Robert. 1997. "Kinesthetic-Visual Matching and the Self-Concept as Explanations of Mirror-Self-Recognition." *Journal for the Theory of Social Behavior*. 27. 101-123.

OUREI. 2006. OUREI Holds Successful Educational Events to Address Killing of Sumatran Orangutans. https://www.orangutanrepublik.org/become-aware/stay-informed/news-mainmenu-9-31878/56-ourei-holds-successful-educational-events-to-address-killing-of-sumatran-orang-utans

Patterson, Francine. 1978. "The Gestures of a Gorilla: Language Acquisition in Another Pongid." *Brain and Language* 5. 72-97.

Premack, Ann J. and David Premack. 1972. "Teaching Language to an Ape." *Scientific American*. 227.4. 92-99.

Premack, David. 1971. "Language in Chimpanzee?" *Science* 172. 808-822.

Rijksen, Herman and Erik Meijaard. 1997. "Our Vanishing Relative: The Status of Wild Orangutans at the Close of the Twentieth Century." Stichting Tropenbos. Online.

Román, Valeria. 2015. "Argentina Grants an Orangutan human-like Rights." *Scientific American*. https://www.scientificamerican.com/article/argentina-grants-an-orangutan-human-like-rights/

Rose, Anthony L. 1994. "Description and Analysis of Profound Interspecies Events." *Proceedings of the XVth Congress of International Primatological Society*, Bali, Indonesia.

Russon, Anne E. 2004. *Orangutans: Wizards of the Rainforest*. NY: Firefly Books.

Santika, Truly, et al, 2022. "Effectiveness of 20 years of conservation investments in protecting orangutans." *Current Biology* (2022). DOI: 10.1016/j.cub.2022.02.051

Shapiro, Gary. 1975. *Teaching Linguistic Concepts to a Juvenile Orangutan*, M.A. Thesis, California State University Fresno, Department of Biology.

Shapiro, Gary. 1982. "Sign Acquisition in a Home-reared / Free-ranging Orangutan: Comparisons with Other Signing Apes." *American Journal of Primatology* 3. 121-129.

Shapiro, Gary. 1985. *Factors Influencing Sign Learning Performance in Four Juvenile Orangutans*. Ph.D. Dissertation, University of Oklahoma, Dept. of Zoology. University Microfilms International, Ann Arbor, MI. online: https://ourf.info/images/documents/glsdissertation.pdf

Shapiro, Gary. 1995. "Data and Observations from a Short-Term Limnological Study of the Sekonyer River, A Blackwater Tributary in Tanjung Puting National Park, Central Kalimantan, Indonesia." *Borneo Research Bulletin* 26. 25-53.

Shapiro, Gary and Biruté Galdikas. 1995, "Visual Attentiveness of Orangutans within the Sign Learning Context." *The Neglected Ape*, Ronald. D. Nadler, B.M.F. Galdikas, Lori. Sheeran, and Norm Rosen, eds. Plenum, New York.

Shapiro, Gary and Biruté Galdikas. 1999. “Early Sign Performance in a Free-ranging, Adult Orangutan.” *The Mentalities of Gorillas and Orangutans: Comparative Perspectives.* Sue Taylor Parker, Robert W. Mitchell and H. Lyn Miles, eds. Cambridge: CUP. 265-279.

Singer, Peter and Paola Cavalieri (eds.), 1993. *The Great Ape Project: Equality beyond humanity.* Fourth Estate publishing, London, England

Stiles, Daniel. 2023. *Empty Forests: How Politics, Economics and Corruption Fuel Live Great Ape Trafficking, Global Initiative Against Transnational Organized Crime.* Geneva, Switzerland.

Strindberg, Samantha, Fiona Maisels, Elizabeth. Williamson, Stephen Blake, and Emma Stokes. 2018. Guns, germs, and trees determine density and distribution of gorillas and chimpanzees in Western Equatorial Africa. *Science Advances.* Vol 4 (4). DOI: 10.1126/sciadv.aar2964

Suarez, Susan and Gordon Gallup, Jr. 1981. “Self-Recognition in Chimpanzee and Orangutans, But Not Gorillas.” *Journal of Human Evolution.* 10. 175-188.

Swartz, Karyl. 1997. “What is Mirror-Recognition, and What is it Not?” *Annals of* the New York Academy of Sciences. 818. 65-71.

Thompson, Shawn. 2002. *Letters from Prison: Felons Write about the Struggle for Life and Sanity Behind Bars.* Harper Collins.

Thompson, Shawn. 2010. *The Intimate Ape: Orangutans and the Secret Life of a Vanishing Species.* Kensington.

Thompson, Shawn. 2019. "Supporting Ape Rights: Finding the Right Fit Between Science and the Law." *ASEBL Journal* 14.1. 3-25. Online.

UNEP. 2005. The Kinshasa Declaration on Great Apes. UNESCO. https://www.cites.org/sites/default/files/eng/news/sundry/2005/kinshasa_declaration.pdf

van Schaik, Carel P., et al. 1996. "Manufacture and Use of Tools in Wild Sumatran Orangutans: Implications for Human Evolution." *Naturwissenschaften* 83. 186-188.

van Schaik, Carel P., et al. 2003. "Orangutan Cultures and the Evolution of Material Culture." *Science* 299. 102-105.

van Schaik, Carel P., et al. 2013. "Wild Orangutan Males Plan and Communicate Their Travel Direction One Day in Advance." *Plos One* 8.9. e74896. doi: 10.1371/journal.pone.0074896.

Voigt, Maria, et al. 2018. "Global Demand for Natural Resources Eliminated More Than 100,000 Bornean Orangutan," *Current Biology* 28.5. 761-769e5. doi: 10.1016/j.cub.2018.01.053.

Wich, Serge, et al. 2008. "Distribution and Conservation Status of the Orang-utan (Pongo spp.) on Borneo and Sumatra: How Many Remain?" Fauna & Flora International. *Oryx* 42.3. 329-339.

WWF. 2018. *Living Planet Report - 2018: Aiming Higher.* Grooten, M. and Almond, R.E.A., eds. WWF, Gland, Switzerland.

Addendums

Orangutan Caring Scholarships: OURF first Signature Program

Producing conferences, workshops and ceremonies weren't the only endeavors my wife, Inggriani, and I wanted to pursue for our newly formed organization. During our first visit to Indonesia with OUREI in 2005, we traveled to Sumatra to introduce ourselves to representatives of various orangutan and environmental organizations, including Panut Hadisiswoyo, founder of the Orangutan Information Center (OIC). We were seeking ideas from the local perspective and collaborative projects that could make a tangible impact.

Panut mentioned how it would be advisable to collaborate on a scholarship program for students going into local universities. I immediately got excited about the prospect of encouraging the matriculation of future orangutan advocates and conservationists.

We decided to create our first signature program, the Orangutan Caring Scholarship, with OUREI responsible for raising the funds and OIC administering and managing the program locally. We were mindful in designing the scholarship to ensure its effectiveness and long-term benefits. Instead of offering a full ride, we limited the scholarship to cover the expenses of tuition and research write-up over a four-year period, as most students remained with their parents during their stud-

ies. We wanted to ensure the students were pursuing degrees in biology, forestry and veterinary science, fields that would directly benefit orangutans when they graduated. Additionally, we recognized the need to actively encourage young women to apply, fostering diversity and inclusivity in the conservation field.

In 2006, Syarifah Lia Andriati became the first recipient, marking a significant milestone. Throughout her college years studying forestry, she actively engaged in extracurricular activities with OIC, gaining practical insights into orangutan conservation. After graduating in 2009, she became the CSR manager for an Acehnese bank, exemplifying the program's transformative power.

Since Syarifah, the program has experienced remarkable growth and impact. It expanded its reach, granting over 300 multi-year scholarships in all orangutan-range provinces on Sumatra and Kalimantan provinces. Collaborating with other implementing partners, the program has enabled students to receive scholarships in crucial areas for orangutan conservation. Over 190 students have successfully graduated and assumed roles in academia, government, business, and conservation nonprofits, becoming powerful advocates making a tangible difference.

While robust orangutan populations can't be directly linked to education, the Orangutan Caring Scholarship program nurtures a generation of dedicated conservation leaders. It was designed not only to support educational aspirations but also to empower recipients to become agents of change ensuring this great ape's long-term survival. Witnessing their journeys has been personally gratifying.

The Comparative Study on Sign Learning by Four Orangutans

While I was able to demonstrate that adult and juvenile orangutans could learn to use signs like other great apes, the lengthy sign-teaching sessions with Rinnie and Princess did not form the basis of my doctoral research project. I knew I couldn't spend a decade in the graduate department of the University of Oklahoma trying to convince my doctoral committee that orangutans possessed "language" particularly when so many were hard-core zoologists. I needed to design a project that would allow me to examine one aspect of the signing phenomenon with statistical rigor.

I decided to do a comparative study examining the factors influencing sign learning by four juvenile orangutans and compare the results with a study conducted by my major professor, Roger Fouts (1973), who looked at how quickly four juvenile chimpanzees could acquire and learn signs. Not only that, I planned to improve upon Fouts's methodology and design the study in a way to test the effect of gender, living condition, and hand preference on sign learning. To do that meant I was going to conduct an ANOVA - Analysis of Variance - to partition the sign learning data to see if there were statistically significant differences between the key variables, i.e., would there be signing differences between the male and female orangutans, the cage living and the home-reared orangutans, and the right - and left - hand preferred orangutans.

I would need four juvenile orangutans to become my students and I had nearly a dozen to choose from. This would be a difficult if not impossible study to do in North America, then and now, for a variety of reasons. Additionally, I planned to have four control orangutans to add a level of scientific rigor. These control orangutans would be "gender and living condition" matched to the experimental subjects and would need to have their hand preference assessed. Why hand preference? I wanted to demonstrate the presence of functional neurological asymmetry in the orangutan using sign learning as a probe starting with the understanding that learned hand movement skills, such as those for signs language, are mediated by and stored in motor regions of the brain contralateral to the particular hand. According to Norm Geschwind, a behavioral neurologist, if the dominant hand that could perform a skill, say learning a sign to specific criteria, no longer can perform the skill, then the stored memorized instructions for that skill should cross the corpus callosum to the naïve contralateral hemisphere allowing the nondominant hand to more quickly learn and perform the sign as compared to signs initially taught to the nondominant hand. That differential relearning of signs could make it possible to demonstrate functional neurological asymmetry in the orangutan. In addition, it could show a utility of the sign learning paradigm for more than addressing language competencies in a great ape.

According to my experimental design, I would teach five of the signs to one hand and a different five to the other hand for each student. Then once the orangutan acquired the sign according to the criterion, I would retrain the sign to the other hand after physically preventing the trained hand from performing the sign. A statistically significant difference in the reacquisition rates would provide the data needed to affirm Geschwind's hypothesis and demonstrate neurological asymmetry.

When I went to the safety enclosure and started to choose my students, it was easy to tell the males from the females, and I could assign two to the home-reared living condition and leave two in the safety enclosure. What was challenging was determining the hand preference of the nine or so orangutans in the safety enclosure. I decided to create two independent tests to assess hand preference: the peanut selection test and the peanut extraction test. In the peanut selection test, each orangutan would be given an opportunity to grab a peanut and I would score if the orangutan used their right or left hand. I also gave them a block of ironwood with eighteen holes packed with peanuts. I would score which hand and finger would be used to probe the holes to get the peanuts out. Over time, I came to see that each orangutan had a favorite hand to use. I chose two females, one being Princess, and two males.

Princess preferred to use her left hand in both the peanut selection and extraction tests. She would stay in the home-reared group. A male orangutan named Pola demonstrated strong right-hand preference and was assigned to the home-reared group as well. Then there was Hampas, whose name means "Lost", who was a female with a thick coat of hair. She was right-hand preferred and was assigned to the safety enclosure. Finally, there was Rantai whose name means "Chain". When he was rescued, he had a chain around him. Rantai was left-hand preferred and would stay in the safety enclosure with Hampas.

At the end of the 18-month study, I was unable to obtain the necessary data for every sign that was taught. For those signs that were acquired, some were not reacquired. While comparisons I made with the transformed data to demonstrate asymmetry were suggestive, they were, in the end, statistically inconclusive. My committee suggested the experiment not be placed in my dissertation so it was deleted from the early drafts.

My dissertation results can be found at https://ourf.info/images/documents/glsdissertation.pdf.

Dr. Gary L. Shapiro, began his involvement with orangutans 50 years ago in the field of primate cognition and learning. He was the first person to teach symbolic communication to a captive orangutan and the first person to teach sign language to orangutans in their natural environment in Borneo.

While in Borneo, Shapiro helped rehabilitate dozens of ex-captive orangutans and later shifted his interests to conservation and the ethical issues regarding orangutans and their habitat.

He returned to Borneo after graduating to conduct a blackwater river study and helped establish the first orangutan advocacy group, the Orangutan Foundation International (where he served as vice president for 18 years), and the Orang Utan Republik Foundation, where he currently serves as president.

Contact the author or read the full bio on thmaduco.org:

For any related live events or collaborations, please contact The Mad Duck Coalition through its contact form.

Author Recommendations

BMF Galdikas
Reflections of Eden

EO Wilson
Half-Earth: Our Planet's Fight for Life.

Gregory Tague
An Ape Ethic and the Question of Personhood

Leif Cocks
Orangutan, My Cousins, My Friends.

Paola Cavalier & Peter Singer
The Great Ape Project: Equality Beyond Humanity

And the special works of his fellow mad ducks.

Concluding Note

Thank you so much for purchasing this work! Your support allows us to continue to avoid resorting to anti-consumer DRM practices and encourages our authors, not just this one, to continue following their passions and producing intellectually stimulating works. It also enables us to provide special programs for supporters like you!

One of our programs is a special discount for reviews, positive and negative! We believe that even negative feedback is vital feedback, so you should say what you really think. For more information about our review program, contact us through our contact form and select the appropriate category. In short, if the thought of supporting the authors and our jolly little coalition isn't enough to move you, we offer 5% off your next order for each review you post, with limitations obviously. So send us a message!

Information about our other programs and offers can be found on our website, including but not limited to: complimentary copies, contests, and collaborations.

Please reach out for further information. If you couldn't tell, we like to...quack!!!

The Mad Duck Coalition

The Mad Duck Coalition publishing house is a group of innovative intellectuals who want to publish what they are passionate about without compromising themselves or their work solely in the hopes of being published.

As such, The MDC publishes quality works that intellectually stimulate the mind, not necessarily the pockets. We wholeheartedly believe that quality and commerciality are two different things and that quality is far more important.

Check us out at thmaduco.org: